BIBLE QUIZZES

that

Teach and Entertain

By

J. VERNON JACOBS

THE STANDARD PUBLISHING COMPANY

Cincinnati, Ohio U. S. A.

2734

INTRODUCTION

When quiz programs were introduced several years ago they zoomed into immediate popularity. It was thought at first that such programs would simply be another fad which would soon spend its force and be quickly forgotten. This did not prove the case, however, for instead of fading out, they have come to be valued both as a teaching device and a means of entertainment. As a result, quiz books are eagerly sought, quiz programs are conducted, and quizzes have come to be big business.

The church was quick to see the value of quizzes, and to make use of them in the Bible school, vacation Bible school, and youth programs. Recognizing that it is instinctive for people to be curious, to want to know, to seek and find, quizzes have been used to arouse interest and to provide an incentive for learning more about the Bible. They are a means of challenging, teaching, and testing. They are also the means of affording satisfaction to the one who uses them, as well as entertainment for those who listen to participants in a program.

This book is unique in that the first section is made up of quizzes which bring out the Bible teaching on important subjects. This section brings to the student the great truths which are vital to character building and development of the soul.

The second part is made up of quizzes which both teach and entertain. They are equally good for personal study, class work, or church socials. It is hoped that the use of them will create a desire to learn more of the interesting and helpful things found in the Bible, and to become a master of the Book.

J. Vernon Jacobs

CONTENTS

Section One

Section Two

BIBLE QUIZZES

THAT

TEACH AND ENTERTAIN

Section One

AFFLICTION

True or false.

1. Affliction is punishment sent by God for something which we have done.
2. Whom the Lord loves, He chastens.
3. The Lord delights in sending afflictions on people.
4. Affliction always softens the heart toward God.
5. God is a source of help to the afflicted.
6. All afflictions may be removed by prayer.
7. If we are righteous enough, we will have no afflictions.
8. Christ had no afflictions like other people.
9. Afflictions may become a means of glory to us.
10. Job is an outstanding example of patience in affliction.

Answers: 1. False. It may be the result of our own folly; circumstance; or the work of evil men. 2. True (Hebrews 12: 6; Psalm 119:71). 3. False (Lamentations 3: 33). He does not afflict willingly. 4. False (Exodus 8: 15). 5. True (Psalm 50: 14, 15). 6. False (2 Corinthians 12: 7-10). 7. False (Psalm 34: 19). 8. False (Isaiah 53: 4). 9. True (2 Corinthians 4: 17). 10. True (James 5: 11).

ALTAR

Underscore the correct answer.

1. In patriarchal times (the altar had to be built by a seer, every man erected his own altar, there were no altars).
2. The first mention of an altar in the Bible is the one built by (Cain, Noah, Enoch).
3. The occasion of Abraham's first building an altar was (his marriage, a covenant with God, worship).
4. After the giving of the law, the altar of burnt offering was in (the outer court of the tabernacle, the Holy Place, the Holy of Holies).
5. Only a (prophet, priest, scribe) could serve at the altar.
6. The king who lost his throne for officiating at the altar was (Saul, Ahab, Jeroboam).

7. The altar of burnt offering was made of (brass, silver, pure gold).
8. The lamb which was offered up was a type of (the law, stewardship, Christ).
9. The New Testament church had no altar because (the temple was soon destroyed, there were no priests, Christ has offered Himself up once and for all).
10. A second altar in the tabernacle was for the (offering of incense, placing of money, seeking of forgiveness).

Answers: 1. Every man erected his own altar (Genesis 8: 20; 12: 7; 35: 1). 2. Noah (Genesis 8: 20). 3. A covenant with God (Genesis 12: 1-7). 4. The outer court of the tabernacle (Exodus 40: 6). 5. Priest (Exodus 40: 12-15; Numbers 18: 1-3). 6. Saul (1 Samuel 13: 9-14). 7. Brass (Exodus 38: 1, 2). 8. Christ (John 1: 29). 9. Christ offered Himself once and for all (Hebrews 9: 25-28). 10. Offering up of incense (Exodus 30: 27).

ANGELS

Underscore the correct answer.

1. Angels are (sons of Jehovah, messengers, ambassadors).
2. The name of the archangel is (Michael, Gamaliel, Uriel).
3. The angel who announced the coming birth of Christ was (Gabriel, Shammai, Lucifer).
4. Angels must not be (looked upon, worshiped, feared).
5. The duty of angels toward men is that of (performing miracles, ministering, giving wisdom).
6. Angels always came to earth in the form of (women, men, great birds).
7. The cherubim had (two, four, six) wings.
8. The seraphim had (two, four, six) wings.
9. Angels do not (marry, need to obey, sing).
10. The angels who rebelled against God were (demoted, severely rebuked, cast out of heaven).

Answers: 1. Messengers. This is the real meaning of the word. 2. Michael (Jude 9). 3. Gabriel (Luke 1: 26). 4. Worshiped (Revelation 19:10). 5. Ministering (Hebrews 1:14). 6. Men (Example: Joshua 5:13-15). 7. Four (Ezekiel 10:20, 21). 8. Six (Isaiah 6:2). 9. Marry (Matthew 22:30). 10. Cast out of heaven (Revelation 12:7-9).

ANGELS (Duties)

Underscore the correct answer.

1. Angels announced to Lot the coming destruction of (Sodom, Nineveh, Babylon).
2. When Jesus overcame Satan's temptation, the angels appeared to (bring a message, compliment Him, strengthen Him).
3. An angel appeared to Peter to (release him from prison, send him to Tarshish, demand an accounting).
4. An angel commissioned Gideon to save Israel from the (Midianites, Egyptians, Philistines).
5. To Sarah an angel announced (the victory of Abraham in battle, a sacrifice was to be offered, the coming birth of a son).
6. When Elijah was despondent, an angel appeared to give him (thirty pieces of silver, some good advice, food to eat).
7. An angel saved Daniel by (causing darkness to fall, putting out the fire in the furnace, shutting the mouths of the lions).
8. An angel directed Cornelius to send for (Peter, John, Paul) in order to learn the way of salvation.
9. An angel appeared to Paul to (rebuke him, tell him all on board ship would be saved, urge him to flee).
10. An angel directed (Philip, Titus, Barnabas) to meet and preach to an Ethiopian.

Answers: 1. Sodom (Genesis 19:1, 13). 2. Strengthen him (Matthew 4:11). 3. Release him from prison (Acts 12:1-11). 4. Midianites (Judges 6:11-14). 5. The coming birth of a son (Genesis 18:14). 6. Food to eat (1 Kings 19:4-8). 7. Shutting the mouths of lions (Daniel 6:1-24). 8. Peter (Acts 10:30-32). 9. Tell him all on board ship would be saved (Acts 27:1-26). 10. Philip (Acts 8:26).

ANGER

Fill the blanks.

1. Jesus said, "Whosoever is angry with his brother without a cause shall be in danger of the _____" (Matthew 5:22).
2. "It is better to dwell in the wilderness, than with a contentious and an angry _____" (Proverbs 21:19).
3. "Fathers, provoke not your children to _____: but bring them up in the nurture and admonition of the Lord" (Ephesians 6:4).
4. "God is angry with the _____ every day" (Psalm 7:11).
5. "Be ye angry, and sin not: let not the sun go down upon your _____" (Ephesians 4:26).
6. "The Lord is merciful and gracious, slow to _____, and plenteous in mercy" (Psalm 103:8).
7. "Make no _____ with an angry man; and with a furious man thou shalt not go" (Proverbs 22:24).
8. "For a _____ must be blameless, as the steward of God; not selfwilled, not soon angry, not given to wine, no striker, not given to filthy lucre" (Titus 1:7).
9. "He that is slow to anger is better than the _____, and he that ruleth his spirit than he that taketh a city" (Proverbs 16:32).
10. "An angry man stirreth up _____, and a furious man aboundeth in transgression" (Proverbs 29:22).

ARK OF THE COVENANT

True or false.

1. The ark of the covenant was about five hundred feet long.
2. Noah brought all of the animals into it.
3. A golden mercy seat was on top of the ark.

4. The ark was kept inside the Holy of Holies in the tabernacle and temple.
5. God spoke to Moses from above the mercy seat.
6. A golden cherub was on each side of the mercy seat.
7. Inside the ark were two tables of stone on which were written the Ten Commandments, a golden bowl of manna, and Aaron's rod.
8. When the ark of the covenant was brought to the waters of the Jordan, the waters immediately parted.
9. The ark never was out of the possession of the Israelites.
10. Uzza touched the ark and was turned into a pillar of salt.

Answers: 1. False. It was a small chest overlaid with gold and was about 2½ cubits, or 3¾ feet, long. (Exodus 25: 10). 2. False. 3. True (Exodus 25:17, 21). 4. True (1 Kings 8: 6). 5. True (Exodus 25: 22). 6. False. A cherub was on each end (Exodus 25: 19). 7. True (Hebrews 9: 4). 8. True (Joshua 3: 13-17). 9. False (1 Samuel 4: 3-11). After the destruction of the temple by the Babylonians, we hear no more of the original ark of the covenant. 10. False (1 Chronicles 13: 10). He dropped dead.

ATONEMENT

True or false.

1. All people have sinned and fallen short of the glory of God.
2. God decreed death as a penalty for sin.
3. God forced Jesus to come to earth and die on the cross.
4. Jesus' death was to ransom us from sin.
5. Salvation can be earned by anyone who will work hard enough.
6. Jesus' death was the means of reconciling God and man.
7. Christ was only one of many Messiahs.
8. Christians are cleansed of all sin by the blood of Christ.
9. Every man must pay the penalty for his sins.
10. If a man gives a million dollars to charity, he need not become a Christian.

15

AUTHORITY

True or false.

1. God is the source of all authority.
2. Christ taught as one having authority.
3. All authority has been given to Christ.
4. No one ever challenged Christ's authority.
5. Christ proved His authority by performing miracles.
6. The people were convinced of Christ's authority.
7. If people do not like Christ's plan of salvation, they may substitute another.
8. If Christ is Lord, He must be obeyed.
9. Man may change the words of Scripture to suit himself.
10. Christ gave authority to the apostles to establish His church.

Answers: 1. True (John 17: 2). 2. True (Matthew 7: 29). 3. True (Matthew 28: 18). 4. False (Matthew 21: 23). 5. True (Matthew 9: 1-8). 6. True (Mark 1: 27). 7. False (Matthew 24: 35; Acts 4: 12; 2 Thessalonians 5: 9, 10). 8. True (Luke 6: 46). 9. False (Deuteronomy 12: 32; Revelation 22: 19). 10. True (Acts 1; 2).

BAPTISM

Fill the blanks.

1. "He that _____ and is baptized shall be saved" (Mark 16: 16).
2. "Jesus came from _____ of Galilee, and was baptized of John in _____. And straightway coming up out of the _____, he saw the heavens opened, and the _____ like a dove descending upon him" (Mark 1: 9, 10).

16

3. "Repent, and be _____ every one of you in the name of _____ _____ for the remission of sins, and ye shall receive the _____ of the _____ _____" (Acts 2:38).

4. "Then they that gladly received his _____ were baptized: and the same day there were added unto them about _____ _____ souls" (Acts 2:41).

5. "And he [the Ethiopian] commanded the chariot to stand still: and they went down both into the _____, both Philip and the _____, and he baptized him" (Acts 8:38).

6. "And now why tarriest thou? arise, and be baptized, and wash away thy _____, calling on the name of the Lord" (Acts 22:16).

7. "Therefore we are _____ with him by baptism into _____: that like as Christ was _____ up from the dead by the glory of the Father, even so we also should _____ in newness of life" (Romans 6:4).

8. "For as many of you as have been baptized into _____ have _____ _____ Christ" (Galatians 3:27).

9. "The like figure whereunto even baptism doth also now _____ us" (1 Peter 3:21).

10. "One _____, one _____, one _____" (Ephesians 4:5).

BEAUTY

True or false.

1. Primitive women were not noted for their beauty.
2. The beauty of old men is their gray hair.
3. David fell in love with a beautiful woman.
4. The finest looking man in Israel during the days of the kingdom was Abijam.

5. A beautiful woman without discretion is described as being like a jewel in a pig's nose.
6. Isaac was so impressed with Rachel's beauty that he promised to work seven years for her.
7. "Beware of a beautiful woman who winks," said Jesus.
8. Sarah was still beautiful at sixty-five.
9. King Saul was a handsome man.
10. Vashti was divorced by King Ahasuerus because her beauty was fading.

Answers: 1. False (Genesis 6: 2). 2. True (Proverbs 20: 29). 3. True (2 Samuel 11: 1-3). 4. False. Absalom (2 Samuel 14: 25). 5. True (Proverbs 11: 22). 6. False. It was Jacob (Genesis 29: 18). 7. False. It was Solomon (Proverbs 6: 23-29). 8. True (Genesis 12: 11; 12: 14. Genesis 17: 17 shows she was about ten years younger than Abraham). 9. True (1 Samuel 9: 2; 10: 24). 10. False (Esther 1: 11-20).

BOOKS

True or false.

1. There were few books written in ancient times.
2. Moses never did write a book.
3. A long lost copy of the law was found in the days of Jehoram.
4. Jehoiakim cut out of the Scripture certain pages he did not like, and cast them into the fire.
5. The ancient book of Jasher is no longer in existence.
6. The record of Mordecai saving the king's life was written in a book, and he was immediately rewarded.
7. Only those whose names are written in the book of life will enter heaven.
8. A heavenly register is mentioned as early as the days of Moses.
9. The dead are to be judged out of the book of life, according to their works.
10. The Word of God may be changed to fit the thinking of modern times.

CHILDREN

Fill the blanks.

1. "Even a child is known by his _____, whether his work be _____, and whether it be right" (Proverbs 20:11).

2. "Train up a child in the way he should go: and when he is _____, he will not depart from it" (Proverbs 22:6).

3. "_____ is bound in the heart of a child; but the rod of _____ shall drive it far from him" (Proverbs 22:15).

4. "Whosoever shall not receive the _____ of God as a little child, he shall not enter therein" (Mark 10:15).

5. "The child shall die an _____ years old; but the sinner being an _____ years old shall be accursed" (Isaiah 65:20).

6. "A little child shall _____ them" (Isaiah 11:6).

7. "Thou, child, shall be called the _____ of the Highest: for thou shalt go before the face of the Lord to prepare his _____" (Luke 1:76).

8. "Her children arise up, and call her _____" (Proverbs 31:28).

9. "Except ye be _____, and become as _____ children, ye shall not enter into the kingdom of heaven" (Matthew 18:3).

10. "My son, hear the _____ of thy father, and forsake not the _____ of thy mother" (Proverbs 1:8).

CHURCH

Underscore the correct answer.

1. The founder and head of the church is (Moses, John the Baptist, Jesus).
2. The church is the (building, service, redeemed in every nation).
3. Salvation through the blood of Christ was first proclaimed (in the wilderness, on the day of Pentecost after the resurrection, by Paul).
4. The first "officers" of the church were the (apostles, deacons, elders).
5. The (choosing of Matthias, appointing of deacons, ordaining of Timothy) took place in the church at Jerusalem before Pentecost.
6. It was the wish of Jesus that His followers should (stay in Jerusalem, go no farther than Antioch, go into all the world).
7. People are added to the church by (a vote of the people, the elders, the Lord).
8. The church was at first held in favor by (all the people, the Galileans, the Herodians).
9. The church met together on the (sabbath day, first day of the week, Passover).
10. The rapid growth of the church caused it to be (officially recognized by the government, persecuted, popular).

Answers: 1. Jesus (Matthew 16: 16). 2. Redeemed in every nation. 3. On the day of Pentecost after the resurrection (Acts 2). 4. Apostles (Acts 1). 5. Choosing of Matthias (Acts 1: 23-26). 6. Go into all the world (Acts 1: 8). 7. The Lord (Acts 2: 47). 8. All the people (Acts 2: 47). 9. The first day of the week (Acts 20: 7). 10. Persecuted (Acts 8: 1).

COMPANIONS

Underscore the correct answer.

1. Jonathan loved David so deeply he was willing to (make him captain, give up his kingdom, be his armor-bearer).

2. Samson's troubles started when he got interested in (drinking, gambling, a Philistine girl).
3. Joseph was sold into slavery at the suggestion of (Reuben, Judah, Zebulun).
4. Rehoboam lost most of his kingdom because he (underestimated the strength of the enemy, listened to his young friends, was caught unprepared).
5. Job's friends urged him to (confess his sins, make a treaty, offer up a sacrifice).
6. Paul and Barnabas, when they came to Lystra, were looked upon as (spies, foreigners, gods).
7. The friends of Jephthah's daughter (gave her a wedding shower, visited her, mourned her fate annually).
8. Jesus appeared after His resurrection to two friends on the way to (the tomb, Emmaus, Galilee).
9. The disciples got into a big argument as to who was (the wisest, the most righteous, the greatest).
10. Paul and Barnabas disagreed over (how much salary each should receive, taking Mark with them on a journey, which of them had the most authority).

Answers: 1. Give up his kingdom (1 Samuel 20). 2. A Philistine girl (Judges 14: 1-20). 3. Judah (Genesis 37: 26, 27). 4. Listened to his young friends (2 Chronicles 10: 10). 5. Confess his sins (Job 11: 13-15). 6. Gods (Acts 14: 11). 7. Mourned her fate annually (Judges 11: 30-40). 8. Emmaus (Luke 24: 13-35). 9. The greatest (Luke 22: 24-26). 10. Taking Mark with them on a journey (Acts 15: 36-41).

CONFESSION

Underscore the correct answer.

1. The good confession of faith is ("I believe there is a God," "I believe in the Bible," "Thou art the Christ, the Son of the living God."
2. The good confession was made by Peter in (Jerusalem, Galilee, Caesarea Philippi).

3. The man who confessed Christ at the foot of the cross was (Ananias, Herod, the centurion).
4. The occasion for Martha making the good confession was (a dinner in her home, a visit to the temple, the death of Lazarus).
5. Confession is a preliminary to (partaking of the Lord's Supper, salvation, marriage).
6. If we confess Christ before others (we need not attend church, we may go and sin again, He will confess us before the heavenly Father).
7. The Ethiopian eunuch confessed Christ (in the desert, by the lake, in the synagogue).
8. The man who was put out of the synagogue for confessing Christ was (Nicodemus, the man born blind, Zacchaeus).
9. The one who confessed Christ before many witnesses was (Timothy, Mary Magdalene, Lydia).
10. Paul made the good confession of faith before (Felix, Simon Magus, Cornelius).

Answers: 1. "Thou art the Christ, the Son of the living God" (Matthew 16: 16). 2. Caesarea Philippi (Matthew 16: 13). 3. The centurion (Mark 15: 39). 4. The death of Lazarus (John 11: 21, 27). 5. Salvation (Romans 10: 9, 10). 6. He will confess us before the heavenly Father (Matthew 10: 32, 33). 7. In the desert (Acts 8: 26, 36, 37). 8. The man born blind (John 9: 1-38). 9. Timothy (1 Timothy 6: 12). 10. Felix (Acts 24: 14).

CONVERSION

Underscore the correct answer.

1. Conversion means (quitting bad habits, a change of heart, joining the church).
2. Conversion brings (the forgiveness of past sins, the giving up of all pleasant things, sadness of life).
3. When a person is converted he is spoken of as a (sinner, new creature, saint).
4. Conversion is not genuine unless (a trip is made to Jeru-

salem, one sells his goods and gives to the poor, the heart is right).

5. The first convert in Europe was (Lydia, Dorcas, Priscilla).
6. When the Philippian jailor was converted he (treated the injuries of Paul and Silas, sought to excuse what he had done, resigned his job).
7. When the Ethiopian accepted Christ and was baptized, he (offered up a burnt offering, promoted Philip, went on his way rejoicing).
8. When the centurion was converted he (urged Peter to stay for further teaching, asked him to keep the matter secret, sent an offering to the poor in Jerusalem).
9. When Paul was converted he immediately began to (preach Christ, seek to be elected to office, assert his authority).
10. When one converts another, it is the means of (covering a multitude of sins, having a lot of one's own sins forgiven, making a sacrifice).

Answers: 1. A change of heart (Acts 3: 19; 2 Corinthians 5: 17). 2. The forgiveness of past sins (Acts 3: 19). 3. New creature (2 Corinthians 5: 17). 4. The heart is right (Acts 8: 9-24). 5. Lydia (Acts 16: 14, 15). 6. Treated the injuries of Paul and Silas (Acts 16: 30-34). 7. Went on his way rejoicing (Acts 8: 39). 8. Urged Peter to stay for further teaching (Acts 10: 48). 9. Preach Christ (Acts 9: 20). 10. Covering a multitude of sins (Acts 3: 19; James 5: 19, 20).

COURAGE

Underscore the correct answer.

1. Those of good courage will (find it insufficient during a time of crisis, be the first to fall, be strengthened by the Lord).
2. Moses admonished the twelve spies to be courageous and (bring back samples of the fruit, report on the strength of their enemies, note the number of walled cities).
3. Moses admonished Joshua to have courage as they were

about to enter Palestine because (their enemies feared them, the people were ready to back him, God would be with him).

4. When the inhabitants of Jericho heard of the miracles God did in Egypt (they wanted to see some of them, their hearts melted within them, they did a heathen war dance to gain courage).

5. When the Israelites faced the (Ammonites, Philistines, Moabites), Joab cried, "Be of good courage, and let us play the men for our people, and for the cities of our God: and the Lord do that which seemeth him good."

6. When David urged Solomon to "be strong and of good courage," they were discussing (Solomon's marriage to Pharaoh's daughter, the visit of the queen of Sheba, the building of the temple).

7. When the Israelites had brought the disfavor of God on themselves through (worshiping idols, marrying heathen wives, breaking the sabbath), they urged Ezra to seek God's forgiveness.

8. When the Israelites captured five kings in one day, the leader who urged the people to be courageous was (Abram, Joshua, Gideon).

9. The leader who urged the Israelites to be courageous and do the law, turning neither to the right nor the left, was (Moses, Daniel, Joshua).

10. Paul took courage when he (received a letter from Timothy, was met by Christians on the way to Rome, saw the storm had died down).

Answers: 1. Be strengthened by the Lord (Psalm 27: 14). 2. Bring back samples of the fruit (Numbers 13: 20). 3. God would be with him (Deuteronomy 31: 6). 4. Their hearts melted within them (Joshua 2: 11). 5. Ammonites (2 Samuel 10: 12). 6. The building of the temple (1 Chronicles 28: 20). 7. Marrying heathen wives (Ezra 10: 1-14). 8. Joshua (Joshua 10: 25). 9. Joshua (Joshua 23: 6). 10. Was met by Christians on the way to Rome (Acts 28: 15).

COVENANT

True or false.

1. The rainbow was a token of a covenant.
2. The Sabbath was a reminder of the covenant at Mt. Sinai
3. The old covenant was dedicated with blood.
4. The new covenant was dedicated with blood.
5. The covenant with Abraham was ratified by the presence of a divine light.
6. The Jews had a covenant of salt which they observed.
7. The Jews lived up to their part of the covenant God made with them.
8. The old covenant was given through Elijah.
9. The new covenant is the New Testament.
10. The gospel, like the law, is to be temporary.

Answers: 1. True (Genesis 9: 11-17). 2. True (Exodus 31: 16, 17). 3. True (Hebrews 9: 18-20). 4. True (Hebrews 9: 12-16). 5. True (Genesis 15: 8-17). 6. True (Leviticus 2: 13; Numbers 18: 19). 7. False (Hosea 8: 1). 8. False. It was given by Moses (John 1: 17). 9. True (Hebrews 8: 6; 9: 15). 10. False. It was an everlasting covenant (Hebrews 13: 20; Galatians 3: 13, 24-27).

COVETOUSNESS

True or false.

1. Covetousness is idolatry.
2. The command not to covet is found in the Beatitudes.
3. Covetousness always refers to money.
4. Achan coveted a wedge of gold.
5. The Lord is lenient toward covetous people.
6. The Pharisees were covetous.
7. Christians are warned against covetousness.
8. The story of the rich fool is a story of covetousness.
9. It is all right to associate with covetous people but we must not be like them.

10. If a man is a bishop, he may covet without doing any wrong.

DEACONS

Underscore the correct answer.

1. The first church officers chosen were (elders, deacons, bishops).
2. A deacon may have (one, two, five) wives.
3. The deacon who became an evangelist was (Philip, Nicanor, Timon).
4. The word deacon means (to preach, to serve, to write).
5. The deacon who became the first martyr was (Timon, Stephen, Nicanor).
6. A man should not be a deacon if he (is rich, has unruly children, can not read or write).
7. The occasion for choosing the first deacons was (the neglect of widows, the need for someone to take up the offering, the forming of a church board).
8. The deacons were chosen by the (apostles, bishops, congregation).
9. Deacons should be (handsome, experienced, college graduates).
10. A man should not be chosen as deacon if he has a (sharp-tongued wife, an evil father, a son who is member of another church).

DEATH

True or false.

1. No person has ever been able to escape death.
2. When you are physically dead, you are not spiritually dead.
3. We will have new spiritual bodies in the next life.
4. Jesus is the only person ever to raise any one from the dead.
5. The dead do not know anything.
6. It is too late to change after we die.
7. Our deeds do not stop when we die.
8. Death is not a sign of God's displeasure.
9. Christ's death was the means of reconciling God and man.
10. The second death is in the lake of fire.

Answers: 1. False. Enoch (Hebrews 11: 5), and Elijah (2 Kings 2: 11). 2. True (Mark 12: 26, 27; John 11: 25, 26). 3. True (1 Corinthians 15: 44). 4. False. Elisha (2 Kings 4: 32-36); Peter (Acts 9: 36-41); Paul (Acts 20: 9, 10). 5. False (Luke 16: 19-31). 6. True (Luke 16: 26). 7. True (1 Timothy 5: 24, 25). 8. True (Revelation 14: 13). 9. True (Romans 5: 8-10). 10. True (Revelation 21: 8).

DECEIT

Fill the blanks.

1. "Deliver my soul, O Lord, from _____ lips, and from a _____ tongue" (Psalm 120: 2).
2. "Thy tongue deviseth _____; like a sharp _____, working deceitfully" (Psalm 52: 2).
3. "Bread of deceit is _____ to a man; but afterwards his mouth shall be filled with _____" (Proverbs 20: 17).
4. "Take heed that no _____ deceive you. For many shall come in my name, saying I am _____; and shall deceive many" (Matthew 24: 4, 5).
5. "Then if any man shall say unto you, Lo, here is

_____, or there; believe it not. For there shall arise false _____, and false _____, and shall shew great signs and wonders; insomuch that, if it were possible, they shall deceive the very _____'' (Matthew 24: 23, 24).

6. "Be ye _____ of the word, and not _____ only, deceiving your own selves'' (James 1: 22).

7. "For if a man think himself to be _____, when he is _____, he deceiveth himself'' (Galatians 6: 3).

8. "Be not deceived; God is not _____: for whatsoever a man _____, that shall he also _____'' (Galatians 6: 7).

9. "If we say that we have no sin, we deceive ourselves, and the _____ is not in us. If we confess our _____, he is faithful and just to forgive us our sins, and to cleanse us from all unrighteousness'' (1 John 1: 8, 9).

10. "He that worketh deceit shall not _____ within my house: he that telleth _____ shall not tarry in my sight'' (Psalm 101: 7).

DEVIL

Underscore the correct answer.

1. The devil is a (bit of imagination, real person, sinister influence).

2. The devil is spoken of as being (wily, foul, seductive).

3. When Jesus was tempted by the devil, He (commanded him to leave, called down fire, considered his proposition).

4. The devil and his angels are doomed to be (banished, sent to hell, liquidated).

5. The devil was once a (cherubim, angel, evil man).

6. The devil may be overcome by (agreeing with him, saying magical words, resisting him).

7. An angel who argued with the devil one time was (Michael, Raphael, Gabriel).

8. The devil has been likened to a (dragon, unicorn, leviathan).

9. He is spoken of as (Apollyon, Mephistopheles, Judas).

10. The sword which is to overcome Satan in spiritual warfare is (the Word of God, faith, love).

Answers: 1. A real person (Ephesians 6: 11, 12). 2. Wily (Ephesians 6: 11). 3. Commanded him to leave (Matthew 4: 10). 4. Sent to hell (Matthew 25: 41). 5. Angel (2 Peter 2: 4). 6. Resisting him (James 4: 7). 7. Michael (Jude 9). 8. Dragon (Revelation 12: 7-9). 9. Apollyon (Revelation 9: 11). 10. The Word of God (Ephesians 6: 17).

DISCIPLINE

Fill the blanks.

1. "My son, forget not my _____; but let thine heart keep my _____; for length of _____, and long _____, and peace, shall they add to thee" (Proverbs 3: 1, 2).

2. "Train up a _____ in the way he should go: and when he is _____, he will not depart from it" (Proverbs 22: 6).

3. "The _____ and reproof give wisdom: but a child left to himself bringeth his _____ to shame" (Proverbs 29: 15).

4. "And he [Jesus] went down with them, and came to _____, and was _____ unto them: but his mother kept all these sayings in her _____. And Jesus increased in _____ and stature, and in favour with _____ and man" (Luke 2: 51, 52).

5. "Seest thou a man that is _____ in his words? there is more hope of a _____ than of him" (Proverbs 29: 20).

6. "Children, _____ your parents in all things: for this is well _____ unto the Lord." (Colossians 3: 20).

7. "If any man among you seem to be _____, and

29

bridleth not his _____, but deceiveth his own heart, this man's _____ is vain" (James 1:26).

8. "Be ye angry, and sin not: let not the _____ go down upon your _____" (Ephesians 4:26).

9. "And be ye _____ one to another, _____, forgiving one another, even as _____ for Christ's sake hath forgiven you" (Ephesians 4:32).

10. "Be not overcome of _____, but overcome _____ with good" (Romans 12:21).

DRINKING

True or false.

1. The Bible teaches that drinking is unclean and unholy.

2. No priest dared enter the tabernacle or temple when he had been drinking.

3. Kings might drink all they pleased.

4. If Christians drink, their example will lead others to drink.

5. Drunkards will not be allowed to enter heaven.

6. The people who lived in ancient times did not know the seriousness of drinking.

7. A man might invite a neighbor to drink with him, just to be sociable.

8. A man who thinks strong drink is not harmful is not a wise man.

9. Christians may drink as long as they are temperate.

10. Daniel refused to drink the wine which was offered to him by the king's servant.

Answers: 1. True (Leviticus 10:9, 10). 2. True (Leviticus 10:8, 9). 3. False (Proverbs 31:4, 5). 4. True (Romans 14:21). 5. True (1 Corinthians 6:10). 6. False (Proverbs 23:29-33). 7. False (Habakkuk 2:15). 8. True (Proverbs 20:1). 9. False (Romans 13:13, 14; Galatians 5:22-25; 1 Thessalonians 5:22; 1 Peter 2:11). 10. True (Daniel 1:8).

ENEMIES

Answer the questions.

1. Who was rescued from an allied army of five kings by Abraham?

2. When the Ammonites demanded the surrender of Jabesh-Gilead and the putting out of the right eyes of all the men, who raised the siege and delivered the city?

3. Who used trumpets, pitchers and lights in a surprise attack on the Midianites?

4. Who destroyed the Philistine grain fields by turning loose three hundred foxes with their tails afire?

5. Who captured the ark of the covenant when it was foolishly taken into battle by the Israelites?

6. Who cut off part of the garment of Saul, but did not slay him because God had chosen him as king?

7. When the Egyptians captured Jerusalem and took away the golden shields which Solomon had made, who replaced them with shields of brass?

8. What enemies mocked the God of Israel, and were smitten by the angel of death?

9. What nation conquered Jerusalem and leveled it to the ground?

10. Years later, when the Jews returned from captivity, what nation sought to stop them from rebuilding Jerusalem?

Answers: 1. Lot (Genesis 14: 13-16). 2. Saul (1 Samuel 11: 1-11). 3. Gideon (Judges 7: 16-23). 4. Samson (Judges 15: 4, 5). 5. The Philistines (1 Samuel 4: 3-11). 6. David (1 Samuel 24). 7. Rehoboam (1 Kings 14: 25-27). 8. The Assyrians (2 Chronicles 32: 1-22). 9. Babylon (2 Chronicles 36: 14-21). 10. Samaria (Nehemiah 4).

ETERNAL LIFE

True or false.

1. Eternal life may be obtained by being good.
2. Not all people will have everlasting life.
3. The young man who came to Jesus asking him how to gain everlasting life was Timothy.
4. One must believe in Christ to have everlasting life.
5. Backsliders lose all hope of everlasting life.
6. A person may hate another and yet be saved.
7. Liars will be shut out of heaven.
8. Everlasting life is more important than physical life.
9. Few rich people will gain everlasting life.
10. All who will accept Christ may have eternal life.

Answers: 1. False. It is the gift of God (Ephesians 2: 8). 2. True (Matthew 25: 31-46). 3. False. It was the rich young ruler (Mark 10: 17-22). 4. True (John 3: 15, 16). 5. True (Hebrews 10: 26-31). 6. False (1 John 3: 15). 7. True (Revelation 21: 8). 8. True (John 6: 27). 9. True (Mark 10: 25). 10. True (John 3: 16).

EVIL

Fill the blanks.

1. "As righteousness tendeth to _____: so he that pursueth evil pursueth it to his own _____" (Proverbs 11: 19).
2. "Woe unto them that call evil _____, and good _____; that put darkness for _____, and light for _____; that put bitter for _____, and sweet for _____" (Isaiah 5: 20).
3. "But I say unto you, That ye resist not _____: but whosoever shall _____ thee on thy right cheek, turn to him the _____ also" (Matthew 5: 39).
4. "Abhor that which is _____; cleave to that which is _____" (Romans 12: 9).

5. "Be not overcome of _____, but overcome _____ with _____" (Romans 12:21).
6. "I would have you _____ unto that which is good, and simple concerning _____" (Romans 16:19).
7. "Abstain from all appearance of _____" (1 Thessalonians 5:22).
8. "For the love of _____ is the root of all evil: which while some coveted after, they have erred from the _____, and pierced themselves through with many _____" (1 Timothy 6:10).
9. "Seek good, and not _____, that ye may live: and so the Lord, the God of hosts, shall be with you" (Amos 5:14).
10. "The Lord shall preserve thee from all _____: he shall preserve thy _____" (Psalm 121:7).

EYES

Fill the blanks.

1. "Eye hath not _____, nor ear _____, neither have entered into the _____ of man, the things which God hath prepared for them that love him" (1 Corinthians 2:9).
2. "We shall not all sleep, but we shall all be _____, in a moment, in the twinkling of an eye, at the last _____: for the trumpet shall sound, and the dead shall be raised _____, and we shall all be changed" (1 Corinthians 15:51, 52).
3. "Behold, he cometh with the _____; and every eye shall see him" (Revelation 1:7).
4. "If thine eye be _____, thy whole body shall be full of _____" (Matthew 6:23).
5. "The eyes of the Lord are over the _____, and his ears are open unto their _____: but the _____ of the Lord is against them that do evil" (1 Peter 3:12).

6. "It is easier for a camel to go through the eye of a _____, than for a _____ man to enter into the kingdom of God" (Matthew 19:24).

7. "And they shall see his _____; and his name shall be in their _____" (Revelation 22:4).

8. "For now we see through a glass, _____; but then face to _____" (1 Corinthians 13:12).

9. "It doth not yet appear what we shall be: but we know that, when he shall _____, we shall be like _____; for we shall see him as he is" (1 John 3:2).

10. "We walk by _____, not by _____" (2 Corinthians 5:7).

FAITH

Fill the blanks.

1. "There is one _____, and one _____, even as ye are called in one hope of your calling; one _____, one _____, one _____" (Ephesians 4:4, 5).

2. "Above all, taking the _____ of faith, wherewith ye shall be able to quench all the fiery darts of the wicked" (Ephesians 6:16).

3. "Fight the good fight of _____, lay hold on eternal _____, whereunto thou art also called" (1 Timothy 6:12).

4. "I have fought a good _____, I have finished my _____, I have kept the _____" (2 Timothy 4:7).

5. "Now faith is the _____ of things hoped for, the _____ of things not seen" (Hebrews 11:1).

6. "Without faith it is impossible to please him: for he that cometh to _____ must believe that he is, and that he is a _____ of them that diligently seek him" (Hebrews 11:6).

7. "Even so _____, if it hath not _____, is dead, being alone" (James 2:17).
8. "This is the _____ that overcometh the world, even our _____" (1 John 5:4).
9. "For we walk by _____, not by _____" (2 Corinthians 5:7).
10. "By grace are ye saved through _____; and that not of yourselves: it is the _____ of God" (Ephesians 2:8).

FATHER

Underscore the correct answer.

1. Which father had no mother? (Asa, Ahab, Adam).
2. Which father caused trouble by being partial to a certain son? (Jonah, Jacob, Josiah).
3. Which father sacrificed his daughter to make good a foolish vow which God had not required? (Jeremiah, Jehu, Jephthah).
4. Which father was condemned for allowing his sons to do evil without trying to restrain them? (Eli, Eliakim, Eleazer).
5. Which father, in anger, sought to kill his son? (Saul, Hilkiah, Abimelech).
6. Which father had a son who sought to kill him? (Daniel, David, Doeg).
7. Which wicked father had a very righteous son? (Ahaz, Barabbas, Jehoram).
8. Which father burned his son as a human sacrifice? (Abraham, Manasseh, Josiah).
9. Which father had two sons who became famous? (Amram, Benoni, Cornelius).
10. Which father was the first high priest, and the ancestor of all high priests? (Abram, Aaron, Abihu).

Answers: 1. Adam (Genesis 2:7). 2. Jacob (Genesis 37:1-4). 3. Jephthah (Judges 11:30-40). 4. Eli (1 Samuel 3:11-14). 5. Saul (1 Samuel 20:30-33). 6. David (2 Samuel 15:1-14). 7. Ahaz (2 Kings 16:2-4; 18:1-3). 8. Manasseh (2 Kings 21:6). 9. Amram (Exodus 6:20). 10. Aaron (Exodus 28:1-3).

FEAR

Underscore the correct answer.

1. When Adam and Eve sinned, of whom were they afraid? (God, the serpent, the devil).

2. When Jacob returned to Palestine after an absence of twenty years, of whom was he afraid? (Lot, Esau, Laban).

3. When the mariners learned Jonah was on board, they were afraid because (they thought he was a spy, he was fleeing from Jehovah, there was a law against stowaways).

4. The people of Jericho feared the Israelites because they (were unprepared for war, heard of the miracles, had smallpox).

5. Joseph's brothers were afraid when they opened their bags because there was (a serpent, money, sand) in each bag.

6. The Philistines were afraid to battle Israel in Eli's day because (the sun became dark, swords were longer, the ark was with Israel).

7. Nebuchadnezzar became afraid because (of attempted assassination, of a dream, of seeing a ghost).

8. Belshazzar was terrified because of (spies in the palace, astrologers, handwriting on the wall).

9. Paul's companions on the road to Damascus were afraid because of (an earthquake, a great noise, a blinding light).

10. When Paul was on the way to Rome, fear came upon all because of (a great storm, robber bands, death in the arena).

Answers: 1. God (Genesis 3:8-10). 2. Esau (Genesis 32:3-7). 3. He was fleeing from Jehovah (Jonah 1:10). 4. Heard of the miracles (Joshua 2:9-11). 5. Money (Genesis 42:35). 6. The ark was with Israel

(1 Samuel 4: 3-8). 7. A dream (Daniel 4: 4-7). 8. Handwriting (Daniel 5: 5-7). 9. A blinding light (Acts 22: 6-11). 10. A great storm (Acts 27: 18-20).

FEASTS

True or false.

1. The Passover was the feast of the unleavened bread.
2. Men, women, and children had to go to Jerusalem three times each year for the great feasts.
3. The feast of the Harvest was called Pentecost.
4. Pentecost was called the feast of Weeks.
5. The feast of the Ingathering was called the feast of Tabernacles.
6. The feast of the Dedication came in midsummer.
7. The feast of Purim originated during the exile.
8. There was no feast of Trumpets.
9. Jesus got lost from Joseph and Mary when they went to observe the feast of the Passover.
10. The Lord's Supper was observed by the Jews.

Answers: 1. True. (Exodus 12: 11-17). 2. False. Only the men and boys were required to attend (Exodus 23: 17). 3. True. This came at the beginning of the harvest, and was fifty days after the Passover (Acts 2: 1). 4. True. Pentecost means fiftieth. (Exodus 34: 22). 5. True. It came at the close of the harvest (Exodus 23: 16; 34: 22). 6. False. It was in December, and was called the feast of Lights. (John 10: 22). 7. True (Esther 9: 20-32). 8. False (Leviticus 23: 24, 25). 9. True (Luke 2: 41-50). 10. False (Acts 2).

FIRE

Answer the questions.

1. What sign did God give Abraham to let him know he could depend on His promises?
2. How did God manifest His presence at Mt. Sinai?
3. How did God manifest His presence when He asked Moses to go to Pharaoh?
4. What happened at the close of Elijah's life?

5. When Dothan was surrounded by enemies, and Elisha prayed that his servant's eyes might be "opened," what did the servant see?
6. What was unusual about the transfiguration scene?
7. How was the presence of the Holy Spirit manifested on the day of Pentecost?
8. How did Jesus appear unto Paul?
9. What does the Bible say about the dwelling place of God?
10. How is heaven described, so far as light is concerned?

Answers: 1. At night a light passed between the sacrificed animals (Genesis 15: 1-17). 2. The Lord "descended upon it in fire" (Exodus 19: 18). 3. In a burning bush (Exodus 3: 1-10). 4. He was taken to heaven in a chariot of fire (2 Kings 2: 11). 5. Chariots of fire surrounding them (2 Kings 6: 15-17). 6. A heavenly light shone (Luke 9: 28-31). 7. In tongues of fire (Acts 2: 1-4). 8. In the midst of a great light (Acts 26: 12-16). 9. He dwells "in light unapproachable to physical eyes" (1 Timothy 6: 16). 10. God will give light to it (Revelation 21: 23).

FORGIVENESS

Fill the blanks.

1. "If ye forgive not men their _____, neither will your Father forgive your _____" (Matthew 6 : 15).
2. "Lord, how oft shall my brother _____ against me, and I forgive him? till seven times? Jesus saith unto him, I say not unto thee, Until seven times: but, until _____ times seven" (Matthew 18: 21, 22).
3. "If thy brother trespass against _____, rebuke him; and if he _____, forgive him" (Luke 17: 3).
4. "If we _____ our sins, he is faithful and just to _____ us our sins, and to _____ us from all unrighteousness" (1 John 1: 9).
5. "Blessed is he whose _____ is forgiven, whose _____ is covered" Psalm 32: 1).
6. "Bless the Lord, O my soul, and forget not all his _____: who forgiveth all thine _____; who healeth all thy _____" (Psalm 103: 2, 3).

7. "Whosoever shall speak a word against the Son of man, it shall be _____ him: but unto him that blasphemeth against the _____ _____ it shall not be forgiven" (Luke 12:10).
8. "If thou, Lord, shouldest mark iniquities, O Lord, who shall stand? But there is _____ with thee, that thou mayest be _____" (Psalm 130:3, 4).
9. "But God commendeth his love toward us, in that, while we were yet _____, Christ died for us" (Romans 5:8).
10. "And be ye kind one to another, tenderhearted, _____ one another, even as God for Christ's sake hath _____ you" (Ephesians 4:32).

FREEDOM

Underscore the correct answer.

1. A Hebrew slave was to be freed after (six, sixteen, twenty-six) years.
2. When a young man married, he was free from going to war for (one week, one month, one year).
3. When Cyrus conquered Babylon, he allowed the (Samaritans, Jews, Ninevites) to go free.
4. The governor who would not free Paul until he had received a bribe was (Herod, Festus, Felix).
5. When Lot was captured and carried away, he was set free by (Noah, Abraham, Samuel).
6. When Joseph was unjustly thrown into prison, he was released by (his brethren, Pharaoh, Potiphar).
7. When Jeremiah was cast into a dungeon, he was rescued by an (Ethiopian, Samaritan, Egyptian).
8. When Peter was imprisoned by Herod, he was freed by (an angel, Nicodemus, one of the guards).
9. Paul was a Roman citizen by (birth, naturalization, adoption).

10. When Daniel was thrown into a den of lions, he gained his freedom by (scaling a wall, slaying the lions, the aid of an angel).

Answers: 1. Six (Exodus 21: 2). 2. One year (Deuteronomy 24: 5). 3. Jews (Ezra 1: 1-3). 4. Felix (Acts 24: 24-26). 5. Abraham (Genesis 14: 13-16). 6. Pharaoh (Genesis 41: 1-45). 7. Ethiopian (Jeremiah 38: 7-13). 8. An angel (Acts 12: 1-11). 9. Birth (Acts 22: 28). 10. The aid of an angel (Daniel 6: 22).

GENTILES

True or false.

1. The Gentiles are all who are not Jews.
2. The Jews were not allowed to enter the homes of Gentiles.
3. The Jewish law forbade entering Gentile homes.
4. Paul was chosen as an apostle to the Gentiles.
5. Paul was the first person to preach to the Gentiles.
6. The first Gentile to be converted was Lydia.
7. The Gentiles gladly received the gospel.
8. The Gentiles were not bound to follow the Jewish law.
9. The Jews believed that the Gentiles were outside the bounds of God's favor.
10. A delegation of Gentiles came to see Jesus one day.

Answers: 1. True. 2. True (Acts 10: 28). 3. There was no law against it, but the rabbis demanded it and the people conformed. 4. True (Acts 9: 15; 22: 21). 5. False. Peter was the first one (Acts 10: 44-48; 11: 18). 6. Cornelius, his friends and relatives were first (Acts 10). 7. True (Acts 13: 48). 8. True (Acts 15: 5-31). 9. True (Acts 10: 45; 11: 18). 10. True (John 12: 20-22).

GIVING

Fill the blanks.

1. "Give, and it shall be _____ unto you; good _____, pressed _____, and shaken _____, and running over, shall men give into your bosom" (Luke 6: 38).

2. "Every man according as he purposeth in his heart, so let him give; not _____, or of _____: for God loveth a _____ giver" (2 Corinthians 9:7).

3. "Freely ye have received, freely _____" (Matthew 10:8).

4. "Remember the words of the Lord Jesus, how he said, It is more blessed to _____ than to _____" (Acts 20:35).

5. "Upon the first day of the _____ let _____ one of you lay by him in _____, as God hath _____ him" (1 Corinthians 16:2).

6. "Give unto the Lord the glory due unto his name: bring an _____, and come into his courts" (Psalm 96:8).

7. "Will a man rob _____? Yet ye have _____ me. But ye say, Wherein have we robbed thee? In _____ and _____" (Malachi 3:8).

8. "Bring ye all the _____ into the storehouse, that there may be _____ in mine house, and prove me now herewith, saith the Lord of hosts, if I will not open you the windows of _____, and pour you out a _____, that there shall not be room enough to _____ it" (Malachi 3:10).

9. "And here men that die receive _____; but there he receiveth them, of whom it is witnessed that he _____" (Hebrews 7:8).

10. "Moreover it is required in _____, that a man be found _____" (1 Corinthians 4:2).

GOD

Fill the blanks.

1. "God is a _____: and they that worship him must worship him in _____ and in _____" (John 4:24).

2. "No man hath _____ God at any time. If we

_____ one another, God _____ in us, and his love is _____ in us" (1 John 4:12).

3. "Blessed is the nation whose _____ is the Lord; and the people whom he hath _____ for his own inheritance" (Psalm 33:12).

4. "Thou art a God ready to _____, gracious and _____, slow to _____, and of great kindness" (Nehemiah 9:17).

5. "My soul thirsteth for God, for the _____ God: when shall I come and _____ before God?" (Psalm 42:2).

6. "God is not the God of the _____, but of the living" (Matthew 22:32).

7. "Thou art the _____, the Son of the _____ God" (Matthew 16:16).

8. "We ought to obey _____ rather than _____" (Acts 5:29).

9. "Of a truth I perceive that God is no _____ of persons: but in every _____ he that feareth him, and worketh _____, is accepted with him" (Acts 10:34, 35).

10. "And I saw the dead, small and great, stand before _____; and the books were opened: and another book was opened, which is the book of _____: and the dead were judged out of those things which were written in the books, according to their _____" (Revelation 20:12).

GOSPEL

True or false.

1. The gospel means "good news."
2. The gospel is a message to be believed.
3. The gospel is to be taken to others.
4. Salvation is offered to men through the gospel.
5. Immortality was brought to light through the gospel.

6. The gospel is primarily for people of wealth and education.
7. The gospel will be the basis for final judgment.
8. Those who preach the gospel should do so without pay.
9. The world will end before the gospel reaches every nation.
10. It is all right to change the gospel and bring it up-to-date.

Answers: 1. True (Luke 2:10). The Greek word for gospel literally means "good news." 2. True (Mark 1:15). 3. True (Matthew 28:19, 20). 4. True (Romans 1:16). 5. True (2 Timothy 1:10). 6. False (Luke 4:18). 7. True (Romans 2:16). 8. False (1 Corinthians 9:14). 9. False (Matthew 24:14). 10. False (Galatians 1:8; Revelation 22:18 19).

GRACE

Fill the blanks.

1. "And the Word was made flesh, and dwelt among us, (and we beheld his _____, the glory as of the only _____ of the Father,) full of _____ and truth" (John 1:14).
2. "For the law was given by _____, but grace and truth came by _____ _____" (John 1:17).
3. "For by grace are ye _____ through faith; and that not of yourselves: it is the _____ of God" (Ephesians 2:8).
4. "Let us therefore come boldly unto the throne of _____, that we may obtain mercy, and find _____ to help in time of need" (Hebrews 4:16).
5. "God resisteth the _____, and giveth grace to the _____" (1 Peter 5:5).
6. "Grow in _____, and in the knowledge of our Lord and Saviour Jesus Christ" (2 Peter 3:18).
7. "My grace is sufficient for thee: for my _____ is made perfect in weakness" (2 Corinthians 12:9).
8. "The grace of the Lord Jesus Christ, and the _____ of God, and the _____ of the Holy Ghost, be with you all" (2 Corinthians 13:14).

9. "Let your speech be alway with grace, seasoned with _____, that ye may know how ye ought to answer every man" (Colossians 4:6).

10. "Being justified freely by his grace through the _____ that is in Christ Jesus" (Romans 3:24).

HAIR

Underscore the correct answer.

1. Esau was noted for having (red, blond, black) hair.

2. It was forbidden (priests, prophets, kings) to shave their heads.

3. The (Nazarite, Sadducee, Herodian) was required to shave his head and burn the hair in the temple.

4. The king's son who got his hair caught in an oak tree was (Abib, Absalom, Ahaziah).

5. The cutting of Samson's hair (made him better looking, caused him to become weak, called for a special barber).

6. The Ammonite who shaved off one-half of the beard of David's good-will ambassadors was (Hanun, Haman, Hanani).

7. Jesus said the hairs of the head are (numbered, a sign of age, to give beauty).

8. One of the two women who wiped Jesus' feet with her hair was (Mary of Bethany, Mary Magdalene, Martha).

9. The prophet spoken of as being a hairy man was (Elijah, Elisha, Elihu).

10. Who saw a ghost which caused his hair to stand on end? (Eli, Eliphaz, Eleazer).

Answers: 1. Red (Genesis 25:25). 2. Priests (Leviticus 21:5). 3. Nazarite (Numbers 6:18-20). 4. Absalom (2 Samuel 14:25, 26; 18:9-15). 5. Caused him to become weak (Judges 16:17). 6. Hanun (2 Samuel 10:1-5). 7. Numbered (Matthew 10:30). 8. Mary, of Bethany (John 11:2; Matthew 26:6-13). 9. Elijah (2 Kings 1:8). 10. Eliphaz (Job 4:15).

HANDS

Underscore the correct answer.

1. The tribe which had seven hundred left-handed men who could hit targets with slings was (Judah, Issachar, Benjamin).
2. The king whose hand was temporarily withered as a warning from the Lord, was (Jeroboam, Rehoboam, Josiah).
3. The man who had six fingers on each hand and six toes on each foot was a (dwarf, giant, zombie).
4. What enemy king had his thumbs and big toes cut off by the Israelites? (Adonijah, Adonibezek, Adonikam).
5. Belshazzar became terrified as he saw the fingers of a (man, woman, angel) writing on the palace wall.
6. When Jesus laid His hands on little children, it was to (punish, bless, guide).
7. Who washed his hands at the trial of Jesus? (Herod, Pilate, Festus).
8. Which apostle was temporarily blinded, and had to be led by the hand? (Peter, Paul, Philip).
9. Who crossed his hands when blessing his little grandchildren? (Jacob, Joseph, Moses).
10. Who deceived his father by disguising his hands? (Jacob, Esau, Isaac).

Answers: 1. Benjamin (Judges 20: 16). 2. Jeroboam (1 Kings 13: 1-6). 3. Giant (1 Chronicles 20: 6). 4. Adonibezek (Judges 1: 6). 5. Man (Daniel 5: 5). 6. Bless (Mark 10: 16). 7. Pilate (Matthew 27: 24). 8. Paul (Acts 9: 3-19). 9. Jacob (Genesis 48: 9-20). 10. Jacob (Genesis 27: 1-29).

HATE

True or false.

1. No man can love God and hate his brother.
2. A person may hate an enemy.
3. One who hates is the same as a murderer.

4. Christians can expect some people to hate them.

5. There are things which God hates.

6. We may return evil to those who hate us.

7. If we love the Lord, we are to hate evil.

8. A person can be hated, and still have God's approval.

9. No man ever hated Christ.

10. Enemies should be left to the vengeance of God.

Answers: 1. True (1 John 4: 20). **2.** False (Matthew 5: 43, 44). **3.** True (1 John 3: 15). **4.** True (John 15: 18). **5.** True (Proverbs 6: 16-19). **6.** False (Matthew 5: 44; Romans 12: 20, 21). **7.** True (Psalm 97: 10). **8.** True (Luke 6: 22). **9.** False (John 15: 24). **10.** True (Romans 12: 19-21).

HEALING

True or false.

1. Jesus could heal every kind of sickness.

2. The apostles could not heal one certain child.

3. The ability to heal was a gift to all Christians.

4. Faith was necessary if anyone was to be healed.

5. Divine healing was instantaneous and complete.

6. Prayer is important in healing.

7. God is the source of all healing.

8. No one ever was healed before the days of Jesus.

9. Healing calls for an expression of gratitude.

10. There will be no sickness in heaven.

Answers: 1. True (Matthew 4: 23). **2.** True (Mark 9: 14-29). **3.** False (1 Corinthians 12: 9, 30). **4.** False. This was not always the case. The cripple at the pool of Bethesda (John 5: 1-13), and the blind man at the pool of Siloam (John 9: 35-38), did not even know who Jesus was. **5.** True (Matthew 20: 34; Acts 3: 7). **6.** True (James 5: 16). **7.** True (Psalm 103: 3). **8.** False (Isaiah 38). **9.** True (Luke 17: 15-19). **10.** True (Revelation 21: 4; 22: 2).

HEAVEN

True or false.

1. Heaven is spoken of as a real place.

2. It is described as a beautiful city.

3. It is the abode of all people after they leave the earth.
4. We will be so changed we will not know each other in heaven.
5. Angels will meet and guide us when we leave this world.
6. We will have new bodies in heaven.
7. There will be no disease, pain, or death in heaven.
8. God will be too faraway for us to see Him.
9. The sun will shine brightly in heaven.
10. We will not have to work in heaven.

Answers: 1. True (John 14: 3). 2. True (Revelation 21). 3. False (Revelation 21: 27). 4. False (Luke 16: 17-31). 5. True (Luke 16: 22). 6. True (1 Corinthians 15: 44, 49-54). 7. True (Revelation 21: 4). 8. False (Revelation 21: 3; 22: 4). 9. False (Revelation 21: 23; 22: 5). 10. False (Revelation 22: 3).

HELL

True or false.

1. Hell was never made for men.
2. It is described as a place of fire.
3. People go to purgatory before going to hell.
4. Those who do not care for the poor and needy will go to hell.
5. It is possible for people to be released from hell.
6. All liars will be thrown into the lake of fire.
7. Those whose names are found in the book of life will not cast into the lake of fire.
8. Hell is a place of darkness.
9. Satan will rule in hell.
10. No man need go to hell.

Answers: 1. True (Matthew 25: 41). If people follow the devil, however, they must share his fate. 2. True (Matthew 25: 41). 3. False (There is no such place mentioned in the Bible). 4. True (Matthew 25: 31-46). 5. False (Matthew 25: 46). 6. True (Revelation 21: 8). 7. True (Revelation 20: 15). 8. True (Matthew 8: 12; 2 Peter 2: 17). 9. False (Revelation 20: 10). 10. True (John 3: 16).

HOLY SPIRIT

True or false.

1. The Holy Spirit is a real person.
2. He is a gift to all Christians.
3. All people who have the Holy Spirit can perform miracles.
4. The Holy Spirit has no interest in unbelievers.
5. Unless you can speak with tongues you do not have the Holy Spirit.
6. The Holy Spirit was to divinely guide the apostles.
7. The Holy Spirit will comfort those who are in sorrow.
8. The Holy Spirit dwells in the lives of faithful Christians.
9. The Holy Spirit was to bring to the remembrance of the apostles the things which they had heard Jesus speak.
10. Blasphemy against the Holy Spirit will never be forgiven.

Answers: 1. True (John 14: 16, 17). **2.** True (Acts 2: 38). **3.** False (1 Corinthians 12). **4.** False (John 16: 7-11). **5.** False (1 Corinthians 12: 10, 30). **6.** True (John 14: 26; 16: 12-14). **7.** True (John 14: 16). **8.** True (John 14: 17; 1 Corinthians 6: 19). **9.** True (John 14: 26). **10.** True (Matthew 12: 31, 32).

IMMORALITY

Fill the blanks.

1. "Know ye not that the unrighteous shall not inherit the kingdom of God? Be not deceived: neither f_____, nor i_____, nor a_____, nor e_____, nor a_____ of themselves with mankind, nor t_____, nor c_____, nor d_____, nor r_____, nor e_____, shall inherit the kingdom of God" (1 Corinthians 6: 9, 10).
2. "Now the body is not for _____, but for the Lord; and the Lord for the body" (1 Corinthians 6: 13).
3. "For this is the will of God, even your _____, that ye should abstain from _____" (1 Thessalonians 4: 3).

4. "For the lips of a strange woman drop as an _____, and her mouth is smoother than _____: but her end is bitter as _____, sharp as a twoedged sword. Her feet go down to _____; her steps take hold on _____" (Proverbs 5:3-5).

5. "Can a man take _____ in his bosom, and his clothes not be burned? Can one go upon hot coals, and his _____ not be burned? So he that goeth in to his _____ wife" (Proverbs 6:27-29).

6. "But whoso committeth _____ with a woman lacketh _____: he that doeth it destroyeth his own _____" (Proverbs 6:32).

7. "Blessed are the pure in _____: for they shall see _____" (Matthew 5:8).

8. "Neither be partaker of other men's _____: keep thyself _____" (1 Timothy 5:22).

9. "I wrote unto you in an epistle not to company with _____" (1 Corinthians 5:9).

10. "Know ye not that your body is the _____ of the Holy Ghost" (1 Corinthians 6:19).

JUDGMENT

Fill the blanks.

1. "The Father judgeth no man, but hath committed all judgment unto the _____" (John 5:22).

2. "We shall all stand before the _____ seat of Christ" (Romans 14:10).

3. "And thinkest thou this, O man, that judgest them which do such things, and doest the _____, that thou shalt _____ the judgment of God?" (Romans 2:3).

4. "It is appointed unto men once to _____, but after this the judgment" (Hebrews 9:27).

5. "If we sin wilfully after that we have received the knowledge of the _____, there remaineth no more sacrifice

for _____, but a certain fearful looking for of _____ and fiery indignation, which shall devour the adversaries'' (Hebrews 10: 26, 27).

6. "It is a fearful thing to _____ into the hands of the living God" (Hebrews 10: 31).

7. "The time is come that _____ must begin at the house of God: and if it first begin at us, what shall the _____ be of them that obey not the gospel of God?" (1 Peter 4: 17).

8. "If the righteous scarcely be saved, where shall the _____ and the sinner appear?" (1 Peter 4: 18).

9. "Some men's sins are _____ beforehand, going before to _____; and some men they follow after" (1 Timothy 5: 24).

10. "And I saw the dead, small and great, stand before God; and the books were opened: and another _____ was opened, which is the book of _____: and the dead were judged out of those things which were written in the books, according to their works" (Revelation 20: 12).

JUSTIFICATION

Fill the blanks.

1. "For Christ also hath once suffered for _____, the just for the unjust, that he might bring us to _____, being put to death in the _____, but quickened by the Spirit" (1 Peter 3: 18).

2. "If we confess our _____, he is faithful and just to forgive us our sins, and to _____ us from all unrighteousness" (1 John 1: 9).

3. "But God commendeth his _____ toward us, in that, while we were yet _____, Christ died for us" (Romans 5: 8).

4. "A man is not justified by the works of the _____, but by the _____ of Jesus Christ" (Galatians 2: 16).

5. "The just shall live by _____" (Romans 1:17).
6. "Therefore being justified by _____, we have _____ with God through our Lord Jesus Christ" (Romans 5:1).
7. "But ye are washed, but ye are _____, but ye are _____ in the name of the Lord Jesus, and by the Spirit of our God" (1 Corinthians 6:11).
8. "Much more then, being now _____ by his _____, we shall be saved from _____ through him" (Romans 5:9).
9. "For ye are bought with a _____" (1 Corinthians 6:20).
10. "He died for all, that they which live should not henceforth live unto _____, but unto him which died for them, and _____ again" (2 Corinthians 5:15).

LORD'S SUPPER

Underscore the correct answer.

1. The Lord's Supper was instituted (on Pentecost, the night when Jesus was betrayed, during the exile).
2. The purpose was to (add reverence to the church service, remind people of Christ's sacrifice, give church officers something to do).
3. During the first century the Lord's Supper was held (every first day of the week, once each month, once each quarter).
4. If a person is to partake of the Lord's Supper he should (confess his sins to the people, examine his own heart, have his church pledge paid).
5. This memorial is to be observed (as long as seems desirable, till A.D. 2000, until Christ comes).
6. An unrepentant backslider who partakes (will have all sins forgiven, will bring condemnation on himself, will have a guilty conscience).

7. The bread represents (manna from heaven, the Bread of Life, Christ's broken body).
8. The Lord's Supper is (the Passover, the feast of Tabernacles, an entirely new feast).
9. The first observance of the Lord's Supper was marred for Jesus by (the shadow of the cross, the presence of a hypocite, weariness of body).
10. The first Lord's Supper was concluded with a (hymn, prayer, chant).

Answers: 1. The night when Jesus was betrayed (1 Corinthians 11: 23). 2. Remind people of Christ's sacrifice (Luke 22: 19, 20). 3. Every first day of the week (Acts 20: 7, plus the testimony of Justin Martyr and other early writers). 4. Examine his own heart (1 Corinthians 11: 28, 29). 5. Until Christ comes (1 Corinthians 11: 26). 6. Will bring condemnation on himself (1 Corinthians 11: 27-29). 7. Christ's broken body (1 Corinthians 11: 24). 8. An entirely new feast; it was instituted after the eating of the Passover. 9. The presence of a hypocrite (Luke 22: 19-23). 10. Hymn (Matthew 26: 30).

MARRIAGE

True or false.

1. God is the founder of marriage.
2. Unless a marriage is in the church and the Bible is used, it is not valid.
3. Marriage is on a lower plane than virginity.
4. It is really a sin to marry.
5. Marriage is only for this life.
6. If a woman's husband dies, she may not remarry.
7. Polygamy was not part of God's plan.
8. God does not approve of divorce.
9. Jesus allows divorce only on grounds of adultery.
10. Christians are to marry only Christians.

Answers: 1. True (Genesis 2: 21-24; Matthew 19: 4-6). 2. False. There is no marriage ceremony in the Bible, and for many years after the church was founded, there were no church buildings. 3. False (Hebrews 13: 4). 4. False (1 Corinthians 7: 28). Paul, at one time, said that on account of persecutions and danger it was better if people stayed single, but he never disapproved of marriage. 5. True (Matthew 22: 23-30). 6. False (Romans 7: 2, 3). 7. True (Matthew 19: 4-6). 8. True (Matthew 19: 3-9). 9. True (Matthew 5: 32). 10. True (2 Corinthians 6: 14; 1 Corinthians 7: 39).

MEMORIALS

Underscore the correct answer.

1. The rainbow was a memorial of (the veil in the tabernacle, the promise to Abraham, God's covenant).
2. The Passover was a memorial of (deliverance from Egypt, creation, forgiveness of sins).
3. The monument of twelve stones at Gilgal was a memorial of (the twelve tribes, the passing over Jordan, the twelve apostles).
4. The stone called "Ebenezer" was a memorial of (victory over the Philistines, a faithful servant, the flood).
5. The Lord's Supper is a memorial of (the Passover, Christ's death, the feast in Bethany).
6. The feast of Purim is a memorial of (the saving of the Jews from their enemies, the dedication of the temple, sanctification).
7. The story of the anointing of Jesus in the house of Simon, the leper, was to be a perpetual memorial for (Mary of Bethany, Martha, Mary Magdalene).
8. The golden bowl of manna in the ark of the covenant was to remind the Jews that (God had fed them in the wilderness, heavenly manna is better than earthly food, they will be fed in heaven).
9. Aaron's rod which budded, was to be a reminder of the (authority of Aaron, miraculous power of God, need for ornamental beauty).
10. Of whom was it said, "Thy prayers and thine alms are come up for a memorial before God"? (Timothy, Peter, Cornelius).

Answers: 1. God's covenant (Genesis 9: 11-17). 2. Deliverance from Egypt (Exodus 12). 3. The passing over Jordan (Joshua 4). 4. Victory over the Philistines (1 Samuel 7: 12-14). 5. Christ's death (Luke 22: 19, 20). 6. The saving of the Jews from their enemies (Esther 9: 20-32). 7. Mary of Bethany (John 12: 1-9; Mark 14: 3-9). 8. God had fed them in the wilderness (Exodus 16: 32-34). 9. Authority of Aaron (Numbers 17: 1-10; Hebrews 9: 4). 10. Cornelius (Acts 10:4).

MONEY

True or false.

1. Jesus once told the story of laborers who received a penny a day.
2. Joseph was sold for thirty pieces of silver.
3. The poor widow gave her last two farthings to the Lord.
4. The atonement money was a half-shekel, no more, no less.
5. A farthing would buy three sparrows.
6. Solomon's yearly income was one thousand talents of gold.
7. Jesus said, "Ye cannot serve God and money."
8. During the Babylonian invasion, Jeremiah bought a field for as little as 17 shekels of silver.
9. David had collected one million talents of silver to assist in building the temple.
10. The books of sorcery destroyed in the big bonfire at Ephesus were valued at fifty thousands pieces of silver.

Answers: 1. True (Matthew 20: 2). The Greek word translated "penny" is *drachma*, which was worth 17c, the standard daily wage for labor. 2. False (Genesis 37: 28). 3. False (Mark 12: 42). She gave two mites, which equal one farthing. 4. True (Exodus 30: 12-16). 5. False (Matthew 10: 29). 6. False (1 Kings 10: 14). 7. True (Luke 16: 13). "Mammon" means "money." 8. True (Jeremiah 32: 6-15). 9. True (1 Chronicles 22: 14). 10. True (Acts 19: 19).

MOTHERS

Underscore the correct answer.

1. What mother took her child, as soon as he was weaned, to be reared in the tabernacle (Hannah, Dorcas, Ruth).

2. What mother set her child adrift on the Nile in an ark of bulrushes? (Leah, Jochebed, Esther).
3. Of whom was it said that she was "the mother of all living"? (Sarah, Mary, Eve).
4. Whose mother-in-law was healed by Jesus? (Bernice's, Rhoda's, Peter's).
5. What mother urged her child to commit a crime? (Herodias, Lydia, Michal).
6. What mother was amazed at her son's actions when he was twelve years old? (Mary, Elisabeth, Susanna).
7. What mother had a son who became Paul's chief helper? (Eunice, Lois, Miriam).
8. Whose mother was so evil her son would not let her be queen? (Asa, Ahab, Azariah).
9. Which mother is mentioned as having twins? (Rachel, Rebekah, Abigail).
10. Whose mother sought to kill all her children in order to be ruler in Judah? (Ahaziah, Joab, Hezekiah).

Answers: 1. Hannah (1 Samuel 1: 24). 2. Jochebed (Exodus 2: 2-4; 6: 20). 3. Eve (Genesis 3: 20). 4. Peter's (Matthew 8: 14). 5. Herodias (Matthew 14: 8). 6. Mary (Luke 2: 47-51). 7. Eunice (2 Timothy 1: 5). 8. Asa (1 Kings 15: 13). 9. Rebekah (Genesis 25: 20-24). 10. Ahaziah (2 Chronicles 22: 10).

PROFANITY

Underscore the correct answer.

1. A profane man is one who (swears, is irreverent, has contempt for holy things).
2. Esau was called a profane man because he (cursed his father, sold his birthright, refused to pay tithes).
3. If anyone cursed his father or mother, the Jewish law required him to be (whipped, rebuked, put to death).
4. The command not to profane the name of the Lord is found in (Psalm 23, the Beatitudes, the Ten Commandments).

5. The Sabbath Day was profaned by (laughing, going visiting, selling merchandise).
6. Some Jews were profane because they (told lies, offered up sick animals as sacrifices, stole from the Gentiles).
7. Jesus permitted people to swear (not at all, by heaven, by their beards).
8. Any man who profaned the ordinance of the Lord by eating holy things when ceremonially unclean, was (put to death, thrown into prison, fined thirty pieces of silver).
9. Curses are to be returned with (doubled fists, blessings, a haughty look).
10. Solomon characterized his generation as one that cursed (parents, enemies, God).

Answers: 1. All three answers are correct. 2. Sold his birthright (Hebrews 12: 16). 3. Put to death (Leviteus 20: 9). 4. Ten Commandments (Exodus 20: 7). 5. Selling merchandise (Nehemiah 13: 15-18). 6. Offered up sick animals as sacrifices (Malachi 1: 11-13; Leviticus 22: 20-25). 7. Not at all (Matthew 5: 34-37). 8. Put to death (Leviticus 22: 6-9). 9. Blessings (Romans 12: 14). 10. Parents (Proverbs 30: 11).

SABBATH

True or false.

1. The Sabbath Day was the seventh day of the week.
2. The penalty for working on the Sabbath Day was death.
3. The Sabbath was only for the Jews.
4. No work of mercy could be performed on the Sabbath Day.
5. The Sabbath was a reminder that God had brought the Israelites from Egyptian bondage.
6. Jesus was bound to observe the Sabbath Day.
7. Jesus was raised from the dead on the Sabbath Day.
8. The New Testament church observed the Sabbath Day.
9. The Sabbath Day went out with the law.
10. The Lord's Day and the Sabbath Day are the same.

Answers: 1. True (Exodus 20: 10). 2. True (Numbers 15: 32-35; Exodus 31: 15). 3. True (Acts 15: 6-11; Exodus 31: 16, 17). 4. False

(Luke 18: 15). 5. True (Deuteronomy 5: 15). 6. False. He created the Sabbath, was "Lord of the Sabbath," and was not bound by it (Luke 6: 1-5). 7. False. It was the first day of the week (Mark 16: 1-6). 8. False. Some Jews went on observing the Sabbath Day, which was not forbidden them, but when they demanded that Gentile Christians be forced to keep the whole law, including the Sabbath Day, the matter was brought up in a conference in Jerusalem, and the apostles and elders ruled that the Gentiles were not bound by the law (Acts 15: 1-31). 9. True (Colossians 2: 14-16). 10. False (Revelation 1: 10). The Lord's Day was the first day; the Sabbath was the seventh. The Lord's Day was to remind people of the resurrection; the Sabbath was to remind the Jews of release from bondage. The Sabbath Day was observed by rest; the Lord's Day by worship. (Nowhere in the New Testament is the Lord's Day spoken of as a day of rest).

SONGS

Underscore the correct answer.

1. When Moses and Joshua came down from Mt. Sinai, the people were singing around (the brazen serpent, a golden calf, an idol).

2. What couple sang songs while in prison? (David and Jonathan, Paul and Silas, Timothy and Titus).

3. Who wrote the song starting, ''The heavens declare the glory of God''? (Asaph, David, Korah).

4. Psalms, hymns, and spiritual songs were to be sung by (the priests, Christians, the Pharisees).

5. Jesus sang with the disciples (at the feast in Bethany, in the upper room, in Gethsemane).

6. Who was the author of 1005 songs? (David, Solomon, Hezekiah).

7. Who demanded of the Jews that they sing the songs of Zion? (Midianites, Pharaoh, Babylonians).

8. Who wrote the song in which God is spoken of as ''the rock of my salvation''? (Moses, Solomon, Paul).

9. In heaven they will sing the song of (Moses and the Lamb, We've a Story to Tell to the Nations, Faith Triumphant).

10. Who spoke about "the morning stars singing together"?
(Job, Ezekiel, Hosea).

Answers: 1. A golden calf (Exodus 32: 18). 2. Paul and Silas (Acts
16: 25). 3. David (Psalm 19: 1). 4. Christians (Colossians 3: 16). 5.
In the upper room (Mark 14: 14-26). 6. Solomon (1 Kings 4: 32). 7.
Babylonians (Psalm 137: 1-3). 8. Moses (Deuteronomy 31: 30; 32: 15).
9. Moses and the Lamb (Revelation 15: 3). 10. Job (Job 38: 7).

SPIRIT

Fill the blanks.

1. "God is a _____ : and they that _____ him
must worship him in spirit and in truth" (John 4: 24).

2. "The words that I speak unto you, they are _____.
and they are _____" (John 6: 63).

3. "Except a man be born of _____ and of the
_____, he cannot enter into the kingdom of God"
(John 3: 5).

4. "Now if any man have not the _____ of Christ, he
is none of his" (Romans 8: 9).

5. "He that soweth to his flesh shall of the flesh reap
_____ ; but he that soweth to the _____ shall
of the Spirit reap life everlasting" (Galatians 6: 8).

6. "And be not drunk with wine, wherein is excess; but
be filled with the _____" (Ephesians 5: 18).

7. "The _____ killeth, but the _____ giveth life"
(2 Corinthians 3: 6).

8. "The spirit indeed is _____, but the flesh is
_____" (Matthew 26: 41).

9. "He that is slow to _____ is better than the mighty;
and he that _____ his spirit than he that taketh a
city" (Proverbs 16: 32).

10. "The _____ of man is the _____ of the Lord"
(Proverbs 20: 27).

STARS

Underscore the correct answer.

1. The sun, moon, and stars were brought forth on the (first, fourth, seventh) day of creation.
2. The stars were not to be (worshiped, counted, admired).
3. The star of Bethlehem was (a conjunction of planets, a comet, a supernatural star).
4. A star was to arise out of (Jacob, Judah, the East).
5. When God issues a decree the astrologers (predict its outcome, are powerless to change it, admit they are wrong).
6. Christ calls Himself the (Evening Star, Bright and Morning Star, the Pole Star).
7. The star which the Wise-men followed went before them after they (began to doubt, stopped in Jerusalem, consulted a soothsayer).
8. Those who shine as the stars are (the apostles, those who win others, those who master themselves).
9. In Revelation, Christ is spoken of as the one having (one, seven, twelve) stars in His hand.
10. When the stars fall from heaven (new lights will replace them, the time of the end is at hand, it will be an optical illusion).

Answers: 1. Fourth (Genesis 1: 14-19). 2. Worshiped (Deuteronomy 4: 19). 3. A supernatural star (Matthew 2: 9). 4. Jacob (Numbers 24: 17). 5. Are powerless to change it (Isaiah 47: 13). 6. Bright and Morning Star (Revelation 22: 16). 7. Stopped in Jerusalem (Matthew 2: 9, 10). 8. Those who win others (Daniel 12: 3). 9. Seven (Revelation 1: 16). 10. The time of the end is at hand (Matthew 24: 29).

STEALING

Fill the blanks.

1. "Give me neither poverty nor _____; feed me with food convenient for me: lest I be _____, and deny

thee, and say, Who is the Lord? or lest I be poor, and
——————, and take the name of my God in vain"
(Proverbs 30:8, 9).

2. "Whoso is ——————— with a thief hateth his own soul"
(Proverbs 29:24).

3. "Stolen waters are ——————, and bread eaten in secret
is ——————. But he knoweth not that the dead are there;
and that her guests are in the ——————— of hell" (Proverbs 9:17, 18).

4. "Let him that stole ——————— no more: but rather let
him labour, working with his hands" (Ephesians 4:28).

5. "Let none of you suffer as a murderer, or as a ———————,
or as an evildoer, or as a ——————— in other men's
matters" (1 Peter 4:15).

6. "My house shall be called the house of ———————; but ye
have made it a den of ———————" (Matthew 21:13).

7. "Lay not up for yourselves ——————— upon earth,
where moth and rust doth corrupt, and where ———————
break through and ———————: but lay up for yourselves
treasures in ———————" (Matthew 6:19, 20).

8. "Will a man rob God? Yet ye have ——————— me. But
ye say, Wherein have we ——————— thee? In tithes and
offerings" (Malachi 3:8).

9. "He that entereth not by the ——————— into the sheep-
fold, but climbeth up some other ———————, the same is
a thief and a robber" (John 10:1).

10. "Thou shalt ——————— steal" (Exodus 20:15).

TITHING

Underscore the correct answer.

1. The first person mentioned in the Bible as paying tithes
was (Abraham, Moses, Elijah).

2. Jacob promised to pay tithes to God if He would (forgive,
bless, enrich) him.

3. The tithe of the land, grain and fruit, was claimed by the (priest, Jehovah, king).
4. God claimed the people (despised, ignored, robbed) Him by not bringing in the tithe.
5. In the matter of the Pharisees tithing, Jesus (approved, annuled, forbade) it.
6. In the New Testament church, the Christians (disregarded tithing, laid by as God prospered them, gave little) to the church.
7. Every tenth animal, as the flock was counted, was to be holy unto the Lord (if sick, if the best, whether good or bad).
8. Because the Jews failed to bring the tithes to God, they brought (a curse, a bad reputation, a plague) on the nation.
9. The tithe made possible the attendance at the (synagogue school, three great feasts in Jerusalem, Pantheon in Rome).
10. God promised the Jews that He would (overlook their sins, allow an extra wife, generously prosper) those who brought in the tithes.

Answers: 1. Abraham (Genesis 14: 20). 2. Bless (Genesis 28: 20-22). 3. Jehovah (Leviticus 27: 30-32). 4. Robbed (Malachi 3: 8). 5. Approved (Matthew 23: 23). 6. Laid by as God prospered them (1 Corinthians 16: 2). 7. Whether good or bad (Leviticus 27: 32, 33). 8. A curse (Malachi 3: 9). 9. Three great feasts in Jerusalem (Deuteronomy 14: 23—16: 16, 17). 10. Generously prosper (Proverbs 3: 9, 10).

BIBLE QUIZZES

THAT

TEACH AND ENTERTAIN

Section Two

ADVENTURES

Answer the questions.

1. What adventure came to a boy who was sent to take provisions to his brothers in the army of Saul?
2. What adventure came to Samson as he was on his way to Timnath to see his girl friend?
3. What happened to a certain teen-ager who was sent to learn how his brothers were getting along with their flocks?
4. What happened to Jesus during the time He was in the wilderness?
5. Who went on a boat, and it was more than a year before he was able to get off?
6. What young man was sent to hunt some lost mules and was anointed king before he got home?
7. Who had a wonderful dream which actually came true?
8. What boy started out with a lunch, and ended the day by making possible a miracle?
9. Who took the most unusual ride on record?
10. What boy overheard a plot and saved his uncle's life?

Answers: 1. David met and conquered Goliath, the giant (1 Samuel 17: 17-50). 2. He slew a lion (Judges 14: 5, 6). 3. Joseph was sold as a slave by his brothers (Genesis 37: 12-28). 4. He was tempted by the devil (Matthew 4: 1-11). 5. Noah went into the ark just before the great flood (Genesis 7, 8). 6. Saul (1 Samuel 9: 3—10: 1). 7. Solomon (1 Kings 3: 4-28). 8. The boy with the loaves and fishes (John 6: 5-14). 9. Elijah was taken to heaven in a chariot of fire and a whirlwind (2 Kings 2: 11). 10. Paul's nephew (Acts 23: 12-24).

ANIMAL QUIZ NO. 1

1. Samson set fire to the tails of what kind of animals, in order to burn the grain fields of the Philistines?
2. What two kinds of animals did the Jewish law forbid plowing together?
3. When Absalom's hair got caught in a tree, on what kind of an animal was he riding?

4. In the day of judgment, the righteous and the wicked shall be separated as what kinds of animals?
5. What kind of animals did the priest of Jupiter attempt to sacrifice to Paul and Barnabas?
6. What lost animal became the subject of one of Jesus' parables?
7. What kind of an animal did the Israelites worship at Mt. Sinai?
8. What kinds of animals did David slay when a boy?
9. What animals were forbidden the kings of Israel?
10. What kind of animals was the prodigal son employed to feed?

Answers: 1. Fox (Judges 15: 14). 2. Ox and ass (Deuteronomy 22: 10). 3. Mule (2 Samuel 18: 9). 4. Sheep and goats (Matthew 25: 32). 5. Oxen (Acts 14: 13). 6. Sheep (Matthew 18: 12). 7. Calf (Exodus 32: 8.) 8. Lion and bear (1 Samuel 17: 34-36). 9. Horses (Deuteronomy 17: 16). 10. Swine (Luke 15: 15).

ANIMAL QUIZ NO. 2

1. What kind of animal did Solomon's navy bring from distant Tarshish?
2. When the giant, Goliath, saw David coming toward him, what did he say?
3. When Rebekah came to be the bride of Isaac, she was riding on what animal?
4. Samson is said to have killed one thousand Philistines with the jawbone of what animal?
5. "Can the Ethiopian change his skin, or the _____ his spots?" asked Jehovah.
6. "Behold, there appeared a chariot of fire, and _____ of fire, and parted them both asunder; and Elijah went up by a whirlwind into heaven."
7. What kind of an animal did Jesus call Herod?
8. An illustration of Jesus about "an _____ in a ditch,' has become a much used proverb.

9. A herd of _____, possessed of demons, went crazy, rushed into the water, and were drowned.

10. When the Israelites marched around Jericho, trumpets of _____ horns were blown.

Answers: 1. Apes (2 Chronicles 9: 21). 2. "Am I a dog?" (1 Samuel 17: 43). 3. Camel (Genesis 24: 64). 4. Ass (Judges 15: 16). 5. Leopard (Jeremiah 13: 23). 6. Horses (2 Kings 2: 11). 7. Fox (Luke 13: 32). 8. Ox (Luke 14: 5). 9. Swine (Matthew 8: 32). 10. Ram's (Joshua 6: 4).

ANIMAL SYMBOLISM

1. Who was spoken of as "the lamb of God"?
2. Whom did Jesus call "that old fox"?
3. What nation was symbolized in prophecy by a ram?
4. What nation was symbolized in prophecy by a he-goat?
5. Who were spoken of as "wolves in sheep's clothing"?
6. What animal was used as a symbol of sins which were forgiven?
7. Lost people were described by Jesus as what kind of lost animals?
8. Evil, profane people are often spoken of as what?
9. The devil is symbolized as what animal?
10. In the revelation of John, death is symbolized as what animal?

Answers: 1. Jesus (John 1: 29). 2. Herod Antipas (Luke 13: 32). 3. Medo-Persia (Daniel 8: 20). 4. Greece (Daniel 8: 21). 5. False prophets (Matthew 7: 15). 6. Goat (Leviticus 16: 20-22). 7. Sheep (Matthew 10: 6). 8. Dogs, or swine (Matthew 7: 6). 9. Lion (1 Peter 5: 8). 10. Horse (Revelation 6: 8).

BARNYARD QUIZ

1. Abimelech's servants had stolen something from Abraham which was very important to a farm. What was it?
2. When Jacob was told that Joseph was alive and ruler over Egypt, he could not believe it until he saw something which had been sent to him. What was it?

3. What implement was Elisha using when Elijah called him to be his successor?
4. What bird is associated with Noah?
5. What fowl is associated with Peter?
6. When Abraham's servant appeared at the home of Laban what did he feed his camels?
7. What animal was given power to speak one time to an angry, stubborn man?
8. If animals got loose and were found, what was to be done?
9. Saul's career began when he was seeking what kind of animals?
10. Solomon had forty thousand forbidden animals. What were they?

Answers: 1. A well of water (Genesis 21: 25). 2. Wagons (Genesis 45: 26-28). 3. Plow (1 Kings 19: 19). 4. Dove (Genesis 8: 8-12). 5. Cock (John 13: 37, 38). 6. Hay (Geness 24: 32). 7. Ass (Numbers 22: 28-35). 8. They were to be returned (Deuteronomy 22: 1, 2). 9. Asses (1 Samuel 9: 3). 10. Horses (Deuteronomy 17: 16; 1 Kings 4: 26).

BATTLES

1. What king, more than thirteen feet tall, led his people to battle against the Israelites?
2. What battle was won without striking a blow?
3. In what battle did Joshua command the sun to stand still?
4. What ruler died when a woman threw a millstone on him from the tower of Thebez, which he was besieging?
5. What king disguised himself for battle, but died from an arrow shot by chance?
6. What king brought a million Ethiopians to fight against the people of Judah?
7. What king's son died in battle when his hair got caught in the branches of a tree?
8. What man won a bride by taking a city?
9. What king had his thumbs and big toes cut off by the Israelites when they captured him?

10. What city was defended by horses and chariots of fire?

BIRDS

1. We are told to be as wise as serpents, and harmless as what kind of birds?
2. What birds were sold two for a farthing?
3. What kind of birds brought food to Elijah?
4. What very beautiful bird was brought to Solomon by the ships from Tarshish?
5. The Israelites were provided with what kind of birds in the wilderness?
6. What bird were the Israelites forbidden to eat?
7. When David complained of loneliness, he said he was like what kind of bird in the wilderness?
8. The Holy Ghost appeared in the form of what bird at Jesus' baptism?
9. Jesus said He would have gathered the people of Jerusalem to him as what kind of fowl gathered her little ones?
10. What birds were used for sacrifices?

Answers: 1. Dove (Matthew 10: 16). 2. Sparrow (Matthew 10: 29). 3. Ravens (1 Kings 17: 6). 4. Peacocks (2 Chronicles 9: 21). 5. Quail (Exodus 16: 13). 6. Stork (Leviticus 11: 19). 7. Pelican (Psalm 102: 6). 8. Dove (Luke 3: 21, 22). 9. Hen (Matthew 23: 37). 10. Pigeons and turtle doves (Leviticus 1: 14).

BRIDES AND GROOMS

1. Which girl got a husband simply because she was the oldest daughter, and had to be married first?
2. What girl appeared on the scene at the right moment, in answer to prayer?

3. What older man was pleased because his bride had chosen him in preference to younger men?
4. What man married his half sister?
5. What man married his aunt, Jochebed?
6. What fellow married two girls who made life miserable for their in-laws?
7. What girl was given in marriage in order that she might be a snare, to get her husband into trouble?
8. What young king married an Egyptian princess?
9. What king chose for his bride an evil princess?
10. What girl was chosen queen as the result of a beauty contest?

Answers: 1. Leah (Genesis 29: 26). 2. Rebekah (Genesis 24: 10-16). 3. Boaz (Ruth 3: 10). 4. Abram (Genesis 20: 1-12). For many centuries, close marriages were considered proper. Not until the giving of the law, about 1445 B. C., were they forbidden. People in ancient times preferred marriage within the family, rather than to strangers. 5. Amram, the father of Moses (Exodus 6: 20). 6. Esau (Genesis 26: 34, 35). 7. Michal, wife of David (1 Samuel 18: 20, 21). 8. Solomon (1 Kings 3: 1). 9. Ahab (1 Kings 16: 31). 10. Esther (Esther 2: 2-4).

CATTLE

1. Who claimed ''every beast of the forest . . . and the cattle upon a thousand hills''?
2. Who made a golden calf for the people to worship at Mt. Sinai?
3. Who dreamed of seven fat cattle and seven lean cattle coming up out of the Nile River?
4. Who made reference to ''the bulls of Bashan''?
5. Where is found the law that a cow and its calf could not be killed the same day?
6. Who made two golden calves for the Israelites to worship, one being placed at Dan and the other at Bethel?
7. Where was a plague sent on the cattle?
8. Who cut up a yoke of oxen and sent the pieces among the tribes, ordering the men to battle the Ammonites?

9. If a man carelessly allowed a dangerous bull to run loose and someone got killed, what was the penalty?

10. If a man let his cattle run loose to graze in someone else's field, what was the penalty?

Answers: 1. God (Psalm 50: 10). 2. Aaron (Exodus 32: 1-5). 3. Pharaoh (Genesis 41: 1-4). 4. David (Psalm 22: 12). 5. In the Jewish law (Leviticus 22: 28). 6. Jeroboam (1 Kings 12: 26-30). 7. Egypt (Exodus 9: 3-7). 8. Saul (1 Samuel 11: 7). 9. The bull and the man were both to be put to death (Exodus 21: 29). 10. The owner must restore the amount of damage done (Exodus 22: 5).

CHILDREN

Underscore the correct answer.

1. Paul's (son, cousin, nephew) once saved his life.

2. What boy was made king at the age of seven (Jeremiah, Joash, Jehoida).

3. What girl came to the door when Peter knocked, but was so excited she forgot to open it? (Bilhah, Rhoda, Martha).

4. Job's three daughters were noted for their (wisdom, wit, beauty).

5. Who offered up his daughter as a human sacrifice to fulfill a foolish vow? (John, Jehoash, Jephthah).

6. Whose daughter did Jesus bring back to life? (Jairus, Peter, Pilate).

7. What boy was accused wrongfully of having come to camp to see a battle? (David, Saul, Solomon).

8. What child died and was restored to life by Elisha? (The Shunammite's son, the son of the widow of Nain, the centurion's son).

9. Whose daughter did a dance that was considered worth half of Herod's kingdom? (Herodias, Tabitha, Priscilla).

10. Whose son was rescued by Jehosheba from being killed by his grandmother? (Ahaziah, Jonadab, Hoshea).

CLUES

These clues lead to the identification of certain Bible characters and objects. See how far you have to go to discover the correct answer.

No. 1

1. This man had a very fine vineyard.
2. It was near the palace of the king, who coveted it, and wanted it for himself.
3. The king offered to buy it, or trade for it, but he was refused.
4. The king went to the palace and sulked, lying down, turning his face to the wall, and refusing to eat.
5. The queen heard of the trouble, and promised to get the vineyard for him.
6. Being a very evil woman, she hired two men to bring false charges against the owner of the vineyard.
7. The result was that the owner was condemned, and stoned to death.
8. The queen then sent word that the king might now have the vineyard for his own.
9. When the king went to take possession of it, he was met by the prophet of God.
10. Elijah, the prophet, announced that disaster would come upon the king because of this crime.

Answer: Naboth (1 Kings 21: 1-19).

No. 2

1. This man was a person of fine character.
2. His oxen and mules were stolen by the Sabeans.

3. His sheep and shepherds were killed by lightning.
4. His camels were stolen by the Chaldeans.
5. His sons were killed in a terrible tornado.
6. He refused to blame God for any of these disasters.
7. After these things had happened, a terrible sickness came upon him.
8. His friends claimed that these disasters had come upon him as punishment for something which he had done.
9. He, however, insisted that he had done nothing which deserved such punishment.
10. God finally vindicated him, and restored to him his health, and more possessions than he had owned before.

Answer: Job (Book of Job).

No. 3

1. This man was a prophet who lived in Anathoth.
2. He was very unpopular, because he denounced the sins of the people who lived in Judah.
3. His life was threatened by the men who lived in his home town.
4. Even his family joined with those who were plotting to destroy him.
5. He was arrested, and put in stocks.
6. He was hated because he advised submission to Babylon.
7. He sought to escape from Jerusalem, but was brought back.
8. He was cast into a pit, but was rescued through the kindness of an Ethiopian.
9. When the Babylonians conquered Jerusalem, he was released and given his freedom.
10. He is sometimes called "The Weeping Prophet."

Answer: Jeremiah (Book of Jeremiah).

No. 4

1. This young man was the royal family of Judah.
2. He was carried away to Babylon when Nebuchadnezzar took the city of Jerusalem.
3. He was chosen for special training by the Babylonians.
4. He was a person of character, and would not drink wine.
5. He gained prominence by telling Nebuchadnezzar the meaning of a dream.
6. One of his prophecies foretold the time when the Messiah would come.
7. He told the meaning of the handwriting on the wall, during the days of Belshazzar.
8. He was given a position of great responsibility in the Persian empire after Babylon fell.
9. He had a series of prophetic dreams.
10. His enemies caused him to be thrown into a den of lions.

Answer: **Daniel** (Book of Daniel).

No. 5

1. This man was one of the good kings of Judah.
2. He sought to turn the people from idolatry, even destroying the brazen serpent which Moses had made, because the people were worshiping it.
3. Because of his loyalty to Jehovah, God caused this king to prosper.
4. He refused any longer to pay tribute to Assyria.
5. The Assyrians conquered Samaria, and carried away the people of Israel into captivity.
6. The king even took the gold trimmings of the temple, in order to get money to keep them away from Jerusalem.
7. Sennacherib brought a great army, and sought to get them to open the gates of the city and submit.
8. This king trusted in Jehovah, and refused to do so.

9. God caused the angel of death to smite the great army of Assyria, and Jerusalem was spared.
10. This good king became terribly sick, prayed to God, and was given fifteen extra years of life.

Answer: Hezekiah (2 Kings 18: 1—20: 21).

No. 6

1. This is a small building.
2. It was fifteen feet wide, fifteen feet high, and forty-five feet long.
3. It was made of acacia wood and overlaid with gold.
4. The walls were made of planks, and held together by silver sockets.
5. One end of it was open, having only curtains to shut out the view.
6. It had no roof, but was covered with skins.
7. Inside, there were curtains on the walls, made of fine linen—purple, blue, and scarlet.
8. In them were embroidered the pictures of angels.
9. There were two parts to this building, one being twice as large as the other.
10. The building was surrounded by a court in which were found a laver and a brazen altar.

Answer: The tabernacle (Book of Exodus).

No. 7

1. This is a feast of the Jews.
2. Every man and boy in all Israel was required to attend.
3. Two wave-loaves made of fine flour were offered up to Jehovah.
4. Seven lambs, one young bullock and two rams were offered up as a sacrifice.
5. There were also meal and drink offerings.

6. A he-goat was sacrificed as a sin offering.
7. Two he-lambs were offered up as a peace offering.
8. No one was permitted to do any work during the feast
9. It came fifty days after the Passover.
10. It was also called the feast of Weeks.

Answer: Pentecost (Leviticus 23: 15-21).

No. 8

1. These are mysterious, living creatures.
2. They are not human.
3. They have four faces.
4. One face is like a man; another, like a lion; the third, like an ox; the fourth, like an eagle.
5. They have four wings.
6. They have voices.
7. Their feet are straight.
8. They have eight hands.
9. They seemed to be glowing fire.
10. They served God.

Answer: Cherubim (Ezekiel 1: 4-28).

No. 9

1. This was something which was round, and white.
2. It was good to be eaten.
3. It melted in the sun.
4. It spoiled if kept more than one day.
5. On Friday, however, it would keep for two days.
6. It was ground in mills or beaten in mortars.
7. It could be baked or boiled.
8. It had the flavor of fresh oil.
9. It was made into cakes and called bread.
10. It tasted like wafers and honey.

Answer: Manna (Exodus 16: 14-22; Numbers 11: 7, 8).

No. 10

1. This is an animal.
2. It was not a large animal, but an important one.
3. Two of them were brought to the high priest on the Day of Atonement. Lots were cast over them.
4. One of them was offered up as a sacrifice.
5. On the second, the priest placed both of his hands.
6. Over him he confessed the sins of the people.
7. A man was waiting to take him away.
8. He turned the animal loose in the wilderness.
9. It was supposed to bear away the sins of the people.
10. The one having the animal was required to take a bath and wash his clothes. What was the animal called?

Answer: A scapegoat (Leviticus 16: 6-26).

EASTER

True or false.

1. Pilate tried to avoid responsibility for the death of Jesus.
2. A negro was forced to carry the cross of Christ.
3. A guard was placed over the sealed tomb of Jesus.
4. An earthquake broke open the tomb of Jesus.
5. The first to visit the tomb after the resurrection were Peter, James, and John.
6. Jesus appeared first to Mary, His mother.
7. Jesus changed His appearance and talked to two disciples on the way to Emmaus.
8. With His resurrection body, Jesus was able to vanish at will, and go through doors and walls.
9. No one saw Jesus when He ascended.
10. In one of Jesus' post-resurrection appearances, more than 500 people saw him.

Answers: 1. True (Matthew 27: 24). 2. False. Simon, of Cyrene, was from a Greek colony on the northern coast of Africa. 3. True (Matthew 27: 62-66). 4. False (Matthew 28: 2). 5. False (Matthew 28: 1). 6.

False (Mark 16: 9). 7. False (Luke 24: 13-35). 8. True (John 20: 19; Luke 24: 31, 36, 37). 9. False (Acts 1: 1-10). 10. True (1 Corinthians 15: 6).

FARM QUIZ No. 1

1. Who were the first two farm boys?
2. How often was it required that a farm lay idle?
3. When an Israelite bought a farm, how long could it be kept?
4. How often were farm hands to be paid?
5. What law safeguarded boundaries in a day when surveying was not known?
6. What percentage of crops were to be returned to God in recognition of His ownership?
7. What provision was made for the poor and the fatherless?
8. How old must a fruit tree be before the fruit could be used?
9. Where is a promise of prosperity found?
10. What warning was given to a prosperous farmer?

Answers: 1. Cain and Abel (Genesis 4: 2). 2. Every seven years (Leviticus 25: 1-7, 20-22). 3. At the end of every fifty years, farms had to be returned to their original owners (Leviticus 25: 23-28). 4. All workers had to be paid every day (Deutronomy 24: 14, 15). 5. A landmark could not be removed (Deuteronomy 19: 14). 6. God required that the tithe (tenth) of all income be returned for His service (Leviticus 27: 30-33). 7. At harvest time, some grain and fruit were left for the poor (Leviticus 19: 9, 10). 8. Five years (Leviticus 19: 23-25). 9. Leviticus 26: 3-6). 10. The parable of the rich fool (Luke 12: 16-21).

FARM QUIZ No. 2

1. In the story of the rich fool, what kind of buildings was he going to tear down?
2. What did King Ahab want that caused the death of Naboth?
3. When Elijah called Elisha to be his successor, what did he find him doing?

78

4. The herdsmen of Abraham and Lot quarreled over what?
5. What caused strife between the herdsmen of Gerar, and Isaac's herdsmen?
6. What kind of animals did the Chaldeans steal from Job?
7. Pearls are not to be cast before what kind of animals?
8. Daniel had a vision of what two animals?
9. What misfortune came upon Egypt for seven years?
10. In Gideon's dream, what kind of loaf tumbled into the camp of the Midianites?

Answers: 1. Barns (Luke 12: 18). 2. Vineyard (1 Kings 21: 1). 3. Plowing (1 Kings 19: 19). 4. Grazing land (Genesis 13: 5-11). 5. Water (Genesis 26: 20). 6. Camels (Job 1: 17). 7. Swine (Matthew 7: 6). 8. Ram and he-goat (Daniel 8). 9. Famine (Genesis 41: 56). 10. Barley (Judges 7: 13).

FARM LAWS

True or false.

1. In ancient times, God instructed the people to allow the land to rest every seventh year.
2. In both the forty-ninth and fiftieth years, no crops were to be sown.
3. The farmers were to crossbreed their cattle.
4. At butchering time, care was taken that no blood would be left in the meat.
5. Farmers were commanded to work seven days each week.
6. The corners of the field were not to be reaped.
7. The tithe (tenth) of all crops and flocks was to be holy unto the Lord, and presented to Him.
8. The first-born of all farm animals were to be holy unto the Lord.
9. If an animal had a split hoof and chewed the cud, it was not to be eaten.
10. If a man had a blind sheep or a crippled calf, he could present it as an offering unto the Lord.

Answers: 1. True (Leviticus 25: 3, 4). 2. True (Leviticus 25: 11, 20, 21). 3. False (Leviticus 19: 19). 4. True (Deuteronomy 12: 23). 5. False (Leviticus 23: 3). 6. True (Leviticus 19: 9, 10). 7. True (Leviticus 27: 30-32). 8. True (Leviticus 27: 26). 9. False (Deuteronomy 14: 6, 7). 10. False (Leviticus 22: 21-24).

FISH

True or false.

1. The Jews were forbidden to make the image of a fish.
2. Fish were brought into existence on the very first day of creation.
3. During the ten plagues, all of the fish in the Nile River died.
4. The book of Jonah says that the prophet was swallowed by a whale.
5. A coin found in the mouth of a fish was used by Jesus to pay the temple tax.
6. There was a gate in Jerusalem known as the Fish Gate.
7. Jesus served a fish breakfast to His disciples one morning.
8. The Jews were not allowed to eat catfish.
9. Jesus fed a multitude of five thousand with two loaves and five fishes.
10. After His resurrection, Jesus ate some fish to prove He was really alive.

Answers: 1. True (Deuteronomy 4: 16-18). The Philistines worshiped Dagon, the fish god. 2. False. It was the fifth day (Genesis 1: 21). 3. True (Exodus 7: 21). 4. False. It says, "A great fish" (Jonah 1: 17). 5. True (Matthew 17: 24-27). 6. True (Nehemiah 3: 3). 7. True (John 21: 1-14). 8. True. Any fish which did not have both scales and fins was "unclean" (Leviticus 11: 10-12). 9. False. It was *five* loaves and *two* fishes (Matthew 14: 15-21). 10. True (Luke 24: 36-43).

FOOD

1. How was the land of Canaan described to the Israelites by the twelve spies?

2. What food was provided for the children of Israel in the wilderness?
3. For what food did Esau sell his birthright?
4. What was the favorite food of Isaac?
5. What food did Jacob send as a present to the food administrator of Egypt when his sons went to buy grain?
6. What foods in Egypt did the Israelites like?
7. What food was served to Elijah by the widow of Zarephath?
8. What meat was served during the Passover?
9. When Samson set fire to the Philistine grain fields, what was destroyed?
10. When Daniel and his friends refused to eat of the king's dainties, for what kind of food did they ask?

Answers: 1. As a land flowing with milk and honey (Numbers 13: 27). 2. Quails and manna (Exodus 16: 13-36). 3. A mess of pottage (Genesis 25: 29-34). 4. Venison (Genesis 27: 1-4). 5. Honey, spices, nuts (Genesis 43: 11). 6. Fish, cucumbers, melons, leeks, onions, and garlic (Numbers 11: 5). 7. Corn cake (1 Kings 17: 8-16). 8. Lamb (Exodus 12: 1-4). 9. Grain and olives (Judges 15: 4, 5). 10. Pulse (Daniel 1: 8-17).

FORBIDDEN FOOD

True or false.

1. No Jew dared to eat roast pork.
2. Catfish were to be served on certain days of the week.
3. The hump of a camel was preferred by the Jews to any other part.
4. Goat meat was on the approved list of foods.
5. Pelican stew was a favorite among people who lived near the Sea of Galilee.
6. Grasshoppers had the approval of the Jewish law as a food.
7. Baked opossum had its beginning among the people of Palestine.
8. No Jew ever ate fried rabbit.

9. There was a death penalty for eating meat which had the blood in it.
10. If a Jew found a dead animal, he could not eat it, but he could sell it to a foreigner.

Answers: 1. True. Only animals that parted the hoof and chewed the cud could be eaten (Deuteronomy 14: 8). 2. False. Only fish that had scales and fins could be eaten (Deuteronomy 14: 10). 3. False. The eating of camel was forbidden (Deuteronomy 14: 7). 4. True (Deuteronomy 14: 4). 5. False. This bird could not be eaten (Deuteronomy 14: 17). 6. True (Leviticus 11: 22). 7. False. Animals that walked on paws were unclean (Leviticus 11: 27). 8. True (Leviticus 11: 6). 9. True 10. True (Deuteronomy 14: 21).

FRUIT

Underscore the correct answer.

1. During Jesus' last week, He sought fruit on a certain tree, and found only leaves. What kind of a tree was it? (Orange, fig, grapefruit).
2. On the hem of the robe of the high priest, between golden bells, pictures of (plums, pears, pomegranates) were woven.
3. When the twelve spies returned from the land of Canaan, they brought back a great cluster of (dates, grapes, cherries).
4. Eve is said to have partaken of what kind of forbidden fruit? (apricot, banana, apple)
5. When the Israelites heard the sound of marching above a certain kind of trees, they were to go out to battle. What kind was it? (nectarine, cumquat, mulberry)
6. What kind of fruit did Jesus say did not grow on thistles? (lemons, peaches, figs)
7. Which tree was first invited to be king over the trees in Jotham's fable? (olive, cocoanut, breadfruit)
8. In a proverb of the Jews, the fathers had eaten (grapes, persimmons, grapefruit), and it had set the children's teeth on edge.

9. When the Israelites came to Elim, they found twelve wells of water, and seventy (palm, papaya, pawpaw) trees.

10. When Abigail came to David's army, she brought among many other things, two hundred cakes of (figs, dates, banyan).

Answers: 1. Fig. (Matthew 21: 17-19). 2. Pomegranates (Exodus 28: 33, 34). 3. Grapes (Numbers 13: 23). 4. Apple, though not so-called in the Bible (Genesis 3: 1-6). 5. Mulberry (1 Chronicles 14: 14, 15). 6 Figs (Matthew 7: 16). 7. Olive (Judges 9: 8). 8. Grapes (Ezekiel 18· 2). 9. Palm (Exodus 15: 27). 10. Figs (1 Samuel 25: 18).

GOATS

True or false.

1. No Jew would ever drink the milk of a goat.
2. The tabernacle was covered with a cloth made of goat's hair.
3. The Israelites at one time worshiped the golden image of a goat.
4. Only a ruler could offer up a he-goat as a sacrifice.
5. Daniel had a prophetic dream of a goat.
6. The blood of a goat was offered up as an atonement for sins.
7. The Jews would wear sheep skins, but never garments made of goat's hair.
8. On the day of Atonement, a goat was turned loose to bear away the sins of the people.
9. The king of Greece was represented in the Bible by a he-goat.
10. A young goat, boiled in milk, was considered a very choice dish.

Answers: 1. False (Proverbs 27: 27). 2. True (Exodus 25: 4). 3. False (Exodus 32: 8). 4. True (Leviticus 4: 22-24). 5. True (Daniel 8: 5). 6. True (Leviticus 4: 27-31). 7. False (Numbers 31: 20). 8. True (Leviticus 16: 20-22). 9. True (Daniel 8: 21). 10. False. This was for bidden (Exodus 23: 19).

GIANTS

True or false.

1. Og slept on a bed which was thirteen feet long and six feet wide.
2. Galilee was known as the land of giants.
3. The Zamzummin once occupied the land of the Ammonites.
4. The Anakim were very tall.
5. The Moabites dwelt in the land of the Emims.
6. David fought a giant Philistine named Gedaliah.
7. There were no giants after the Philistine was killed.
8. Ishbibenob carried a spear which weighed three hundred shekels.
9. One of Goliath's sons very nearly killed David in a battle with swords.
10. One of Goliath's sons had twelve fingers and twelve toes.

Answers: 1. True (Deuteronomy 3: 11). 2. False. Bashan and the land east of the Jordan was known as "the land of the giants." (Deuteronomy 2: 21; 3: 13). 3. True (Deuteronomy 2: 20, 21). 4. True (Deuteronomy 2: 21). 5. True (Deuteronomy 2: 9-11). 6. False (It was Goliath, 1 Samuel 17: 4-54). 7. False. (The sons of Goliath still lived. 2 Samuel 21: 22). 8. True (2 Samuel 21: 16). 9. True (2 Samuel 21: 15-17). 10. True (2 Samuel 21: 20, 21).

GOLDEN OBJECTS

1. Who made a golden calf?
2. Who made two golden calves, which were worshiped as gods?
3. To whom did King Ahasuerus hold out the golden sceptre?
4. Where was the golden candlestick to be found?
5. What king ordered three hundred shields of gold?
6. Who stole the golden vessels out of the temple?
7. Who made five golden mice which were used as an offering?
8. What man brought disaster on himself and family by stealing a bar of gold?

9. Who wore a garment with bells of gold on it?
10. Who made a golden image ninety feet high?

Answers: 1. Aaron (Exodus 32: 22-24). 2. Jeroboam (1 Kings 12: 26-33). 3. Esther (Esther 5: 2). 4. In the tabernacle, and later, the temple (Exodus 25: 31). 5. Solomon (2 Chronicles 9: 16). 6. Nebuchadnezzar (Daniel 5: 2). 7. The Philistines (1 Samuel 6: 4). 8. Achan (Joshua 7: 10-26). 9. Aaron, the high priest (Exodus 28: 33). 10. Nebuchadnezzar (Daniel 3: 1).

GRAIN

1. What kind of grain did Ruth glean in the field of Boaz?
2. What parable about grain did Jesus speak?
3. The Jews were forbidden to eat of the grain after harvest, until what was done?
4. What kinds of grain were to be used for bread in the siege of Jerusalem?
5. When the sons of Jacob went into Egypt to buy grain, whom did they find to be food administrator?
6. When harvesting grain, how much was to be left for the poor?
7. What did Abigail provide for David's men?
8. When an ox was being used to harvest grain, what was not to be done?
9. What kind of grain is mentioned by Asaph in one of his psalms?
10. What was the attitude of the people toward farmers who withheld their grain?

Answers: 1. Barley (Ruth 2: 17). 2. The parable of the sower (Matthew 13: 1-30). 3. Until the first grain was offered unto the Lord in thanksgiving (Leviticus 23: 9-14). 4. Wheat, barley, and millet (Ezekiel 4: 9). 5. Joseph (Genesis 41: 54—47: 31). 6. The corners of the field (Leviticus 23: 22). 7. Parched grain (1 Samuel 25: 18). 8. He was not to be muzzled (Deuteronomy 25: 4). 9. Wheat (Psalm 81: 16). 10. They cursed them (Proverbs 11: 26).

HARVEST

1. What beautiful romance budded during the barley harvest in the days of the judges?

2. What man threshed his wheat by the winepress to hide it from the Midianites?

3. God directed the Jews to sow no seed in what year, but allow the land to rest.

4. What provision was made for the poor at the harvest time?

5. In Jesus' statement concerning the plenteous harvest, what did He say about the laborers?

6. Complete this proverb of the wise man, Solomon: "He that sleepeth in harvest is a son that causeth _____."

7. In one of Jesus' parables, at the harvest time what is to be separated from the wheat?

8. What was the harvest festival, or feast of Pentecost, which came fifty days after the beginning of the Passover called?

9. During the year the land rested, what was to be done with grain which came up without being sowed?

10. Of what great event was the harvest a symbol?

Answers: 1. Ruth and Boaz (Book of Ruth). 2. Gideon (Judges 6: 11.) 3. Seventh (Leviticus 25: 4, 5, 19-22). 4. They were not to reap the corner of the fields, nor to glean (Leviticus 23: 22). This was reserved for the poor. 5. The labourers are few (Matthew 9: 37). 6. Shame (Proverbs 10: 5). 7. Tares (Matthew 13: 30). 8. The feast of weeks (Leviticus 23: 9-21). 9. It was not to be touched (Leviticus 25: 5). 10. The end of the world (Matthew 13: 39).

HEROES

1. Who led the Israelites from the Egyptians when God caused the Red Sea to part?

2. Who won a battle over the Midianites without the use of weapons?

3. Who became the hero of Israel by killing a giant?

4. Who saved the people of Jabesh-gilead from having their eyes put out by their enemies?

5. Who killed a thousand Philistines with the jawbone of an ass?

6. Who was thrown into a den of lions for refusing to worship the king?
7. Who saved Egypt from famine by interpreting a dream?
8. Who led the ten tribes to revolt and set up a new kingdom?
9. Who saved David's life by warning him of a plot?
10. Who destroyed Babylon and allowed the Jews to return from exile?

Answers: 1. Moses (Exodus 14: 21). 2. Gideon (Judges 7: 15-23). 3. David (1 Samuel 17: 1—18: 7). 4. Saul (1 Samuel 11: 1-11). 5. Samson (Judges 15: 15). 6. Daniel (Daniel 6). 7. Joseph (Genesis 41). 8. Jeroboam (1 Kings 12: 1-20). 9. Jonathan (1 Samuel 20). 10. Darius, the Mede, in conjunction with Cyrus, the Persian (Daniel 5).

HOMES

1. What man never had a mother?
2. What home was made unhappy because the father and mother had favorites among the children?
3. What home was disrupted because of the hatred of older brothers for a younger one?
4. What king had a handsome son who lost his life in rebelling against his father?
5. In what home was Jesus frequently a guest?
6. What man turned his home into a meeting place for the church?
7. What ambitious mother wanted her sons to have chief places in the kingdom of God?
8. What mother, in order to save her son's life, suggested that he go get himself a wife?
9. What family opposed the use of liquor so vigorously that for hundreds of years not one member touched it?
10. What family prepared a room for a prophet of God, that he might rest there when his travels brought him to that city?

Answers: 1. Adam. 2. Isaac's and Rebekah's (Genesis 25: 28; 27: 1-41). 3. Jacob's (Genesis 37). 4. David (2 Samuel 15-18). 5. The home of Mary and Martha (Luke 10: 38-42; John 11: 1-46). 6. Philemon (Philemon 1: 2). 7. The mother of James and John (Matthew 20: 20-23). 8. Jacob's (Genesis 27: 41—28: 5). 9. The Rechabites (Jeremiah 35: 3-10). 10. A family in Shunem (2 Kings 4: 8-10).

INSECTS

1. Solomon advised lazy people to observe what insect, and learn a lesson?
2. When the ten spies reported on what they had seen in Canaan, they likened themselves unto what insect?
3. What kind of insects came forth from the bottomless pit?
4. During the plagues of Egypt, the land is said to have swarmed with what kind of insects?
5. During another of the plagues, it seemed as if the very dirt had turned into what kind of insects?
6. What kind of insects did God promise to use to help drive out the pagan tribes from Palestine?
7. What kind of insect did Solomon say never could get enough blood?
8. Jesus said, "If he shall ask an egg, will he offer him a _____?"
9. Jesus advised us to lay our treasures where what could not consume them."
10. Samson saw what in the carcase of a lion.

Answers: 1. Ant (Proverbs 6: 6). 2. Grasshoppers (Numbers 13: 33). 3. Locusts (Revelation 9: 1-3). 4. Flies (Exodus 8: 21). 5. Lice (Exodus 8: 16). 6. Hornets (Exodus 23: 28). 7. Horseflies (Porverbs 30: 15). 8. Scorpion (Luke 11: 12). 9. Moths (Matthew 6: 19-21). 10. Bees (Judges 14: 8).

MARKETS

1. When the sons of Jacob went to the food markets of Egypt, what did they seek to buy?
2. Of what was the multitude in need, as they listened to Jesus, and there were no stores near?
3. What tiny birds were bought by the poor, two for a farthing?

4. What animals, being sold in the sacred precincts of the temple, were driven out by Jesus?
5. What animals did Solomon have brought up from Egypt, for which he paid one hundred fifty shekels each?
6. What had the disciples gone to buy when the woman of Samaria came to get water at the well?
7. What did the foolish virgins of the parable set out to buy, and missed the wedding?
8. What were the Israelites forbidden to sell, under penalty of death?
9. What important commodity did Lydia have for sale?
10. What is the most foolish bargain a person can make?

Answers: 1. Corn, or grain (Genesis 42: 1, 2). 2. Bread (Mark 6: 37). 3. Sparrows (Matthew 10: 29). 4. Sheep and oxen (John 2: 15). 5. Horses (1 Kings 10: 29). 6. Meat (John 4: 8). 7. Oil (Matthew 25:8, 9). 8. A kidnapped person (Exodus 21: 16). 9. Purple (Acts 16: 14). 10. To forfeit his soul for material things (Matthew 16: 26).

MARRIAGES

1. Who prayed that the right girl might be sent as a bride for Isaac?
2. Who secured a bride by purchasing the right to her from a kinsman?
3. Who had a wife so beautiful that he was afraid someone would kill him to get her?
4. Who told the story of a man who was thrown out of a wedding service because he was not properly dressed?
5. Is marriage necessary for one to be saved?
6. May Christians marry anyone they please?
7. Is marriage considered lower than virginity?
8. Jesus allowed divorce only in case of what?
9. What mother-in-law and daughter-in-law became models of devotion and fidelity?
10. A woman had seven husbands. To which one will she be married in the next life?

NATIONALITIES

Underscore the correct answer.

1. Abram was the first (Hebrew, Hittite, Herodian).
2. Jacob was the first (Hebrew, Israelite, Jew).
3. Judah was the first (Jew, Hebrew, Israelite).
4. Laban was a (Syrian, Assyrian, Babylonian).
5. Esau was the first (Edomite, Jebusite, Persian).
6. Ruth was a native of (Edom, Moab, Assyria).
7. Titus was a (Roman, Jew, Greek).
8. Cornelius was a (Perizzite, Edomite, Roman).
9. Goliath was a (Midianite, Ammonite, Philistine).
10. Jezebel was a (Zidonian, Arabian, Amorite).

Answers: 1. Hebrew (Genesis 14: 13). All Abram's descendants are Hebrews. 2. Israelite (Genesis 32: 28). All descendants of Jacob are both Hebrews and Israelites. 3. Jew (Esther 2: 5). All descendants of Judah are thus Hebrews, Israelites and Jews*. 4. Syrian (Genesis 31: 20). 5. Edomite (Genesis 25: 30). 6. Moab (Ruth 1: 4). 7. Greek (Galatians 2: 3). 8. Roman (Acts 10: 1). 9. Philistine (1 Samuel 17: 23). 10. Zidonian (1 Kings 16: 31).

*All descendants of Abraham are Hebrews. He is the ancestor, not only of the Israelites, but of the Ishmaelites, Arabs, Edomites, Amalekites, Midianites, Moabites, Ammonites, and Syrians. Jacob, whose name was changed to Israel was the first Israelite, and all his descendants are both Hebrews and Israelites. But of the twelve tribes, only the descendants of Judah were Jews, while also being Hebrews and Israelites. Nationally, the tribe of Benjamin joined in with Judah and were classified as Jews, after the division of the kingdom.

PARABLES

1. In what parable were workers paid as much for one hour, as others received for a whole day's work?

2. In what parable did a man have a son who at first refused to work, and then changed his mind?
3. In what parable did the renters kill the son who was sent to collect the rent?
4. Which parable tells of the birds eating up the seed which was sown?
5. In which parable did the tiniest of seeds grow until it became the size of a tree?
6. Which parable tells of an enemy who sowed weeds in a farmer's field?
7. Which parable tells of a man who bought a farm because of a discovery which he made on it?
8. Which parable tells of a man who passed up a big banquet to go see a farm which he had bought?
9. Which parable tells of a man who went out to seek a lost animal?
10. Which parable tells of a son who could not wait until his father died to get possession of his property?

Answers: 1. The laborers in the vineyard (Matthew 20: 1-16). 2. The two sons (Matthew 21: 28-30). 3. The wicked husbandmen (Matthew 21: 33-43). 4. The sower (Matthew 13: 1-8, 18-23). 5. The mustard seed (Matthew 13: 31, 32). 6. The tares (Matthew 13: 24-30, 37-43). 7. The hidden treasure (Matthew 13: 44). 8. The great supper (Luke 14: 15-24). 9. The lost sheep (Luke 15: 1-7). 10. The prodigal son (Luke 15: 11-32).

PARENTS

1. What leader of Israel was rebuked because his sons did evil, and he restrained them not?
2. What father caused jealousy among his sons by giving one of them a coat of many colors?
3. What parents chose favorites among the children, which led to hatred and strife?
4. Who was the father who resorted to trickery in order that his unattractive daughter be married first?
5. What mother seized the throne upon her son's death, even

killing her little grandchildren but one, Joash, escaped?

6. What father said, "He that spareth his rod hateth his son: but he that loveth him chasteneth him betimes"?

7. Who were the parents who protested against their son marrying a heathen girl?

8. Who prayed for a child, and then dedicated him to the Lord?

9. What mother, by her faith, secured healing for her child?

10. What mother rebuked her son for running away?

Answers: 1. Eli (1 Samuel 3: 13). 2. Jacob (Genesis 37: 3). 3. Isaac and Rebekah (Genesis 25: 28). 4. Laban (Genesis 29: 21-26). 5. Athaliah (2 Kings 11: 1-16). 6. Solomon (Proverbs 13: 24). 7. Samson's parents (Judges 14: 3). 8. Hannah (1 Samuel 1). 9. The Syro-Phoenician woman. (Matthew 15: 27). 10. Mary (Luke 2: 40-52).

PROVERBS

1. "Happy is the man that findeth _____, . . . for the merchandise of it is better than the merchandise of silver, and the gain thereof than fine gold" (Proverbs 3: 13, 14).

2. "He that gathereth in summer is a wise son: but he that _____ in harvest is a son that causeth shame" (10: 5).

3. "As a jewel of gold in a swine's _____, so is a fair woman which is without discretion" (11: 22).

4. "He that withholdeth _____, the people shall curse him: but blessing shall be upon the head of him that selleth it" (11: 26).

5. "Righteousness exalteth a nation: but _____ is a reproach to any people" (14: 34).

6. "A soft _____ turneth away wrath: but grievous words stir up anger" (15: 1).

7. "A fool despiseth his father's _____: but he that regardeth reproof is prudent" (15: 5).

8. "Better is _____ with the fear of the Lord than great treasure and trouble therewith" (15: 16).

9. "Pride goeth before _____, and an haughty spirit before a fall" (16:18).
10. "_____ is a mocker, strong drink is raging: and whosoever is deceived thereby is not wise" (20:1).

STORMS

1. What kind of storm destroyed the flax and barley of Egypt during the ten plagues?
2. What prophet ran ahead of Ahab's chariot in a great rainstorm?
3. What army met defeat and was swept away by the floodwaters of the river Kishon?
4. Whose flight from Jehovah was halted by a great storm?
5. What kind of a storm took place when the Israelites were at Mt. Sinai?
6. Whose sons were killed when a great wind caved in the house?
7. Who told the story of a man who foolishly built his house on sand?
8. Who attempted to walk on water one stormy night?
9. Who wrote one of the most vivid descriptions of a storm at sea in ancient times?
10. What is the greatest storm on record?

Answers: 1. Hail (Exodus 9: 18-35). 2. Elijah (1 Kings 18: 44-46). 3. The Canaanites, under Sisera (Judges 4: 13—5: 21). 4. Jonah's (Jonah 1: 1-15). 5. Thunder and lightning (Exodus 19: 14-18). 6. Job's (Job 1: 19). 7. Jesus (Matthew 7: 24-27). 8. Peter (Matthew 14: 30). 9. Luke (Acts 27). 10. The flood (Genesis 7; 8).

TREASURES

1. Who got into trouble by stealing a wedge of gold?
2. Who made two golden calves for the people to worship?
3. A certain merchant sold all that he had to buy one jewel. What was it?

4. What kind of a cup did Joseph command to be put into Benjamin's bag?
5. What kind of jewelry was given to be melted into gold for the preparing of the tabernacle?
6. Demetrius, who led in a labor riot in Ephesus, made shrines of Diana out of what metal?
7. Where is a diamond mentioned as having been worn?
8. Where is the safest place for treasures to be kept?
9. What parable did Jesus give about a man who loved riches?
10. The twelve gates of heaven are said to be made of what precious material?

Answers: 1. Achan (Joshua 7: 10-26). 2. Jeroboam (1 Kings 12: 26-33). 3. Pearl (Matthew 13: 45). 4. Silver (Genesis 44: 2). 5. Brooches, earrings, and armlets (Exodus 35: 22). 6. Silver (Acts 19: 23-41). 7. On the breastplate of the high priest (Exodus 28: 18). 8. In heaven (Matthew 6: 19-21). 9. The rich fool (Luke 12: 16-21). 10. Pearl (Revelation 21: 21).

TREES

1. The city of Jericho was noted for what kind of trees?
2. When Absalom was fighting a battle in the forest of Ephraim, his long hair caught in the boughs of what kind of tree?
3. When the golden candlestick was being made, the cups were shaped like the flowers of what kind of tree?
4. Across from Jerusalem was a mountain named for the kind of trees growing upon it. What were they?
5. What kind of trees from Lebanon were used in building the temple?
6. What kind of tree did Zacchaeus climb in order that he might see Jesus better?
7. What plant, beginning with the tiniest seed, grows to the height of a tree, and was used by Jesus to symbolize the growth of the kingdom of God?

8. Solomon said, "A word fitly spoken is like _____ of gold in pictures of silver." What kind of fruit?

9. David was to attack the Philistines when he heard the sound of marching above the tops of what kind of trees?

10. The Jews in captivity in Babylon hung their harps upon what kind of trees?

Answers: 1. Palm (Deuteronomy 34: 3). 2. Oak (2 Samuel 18: 9, 10). 3. Almond (Exodus 25: 33-35). 4. Olive (Mark 14: 26). 5. Cedar (1 Kings 5: 6). 6. Sycomore (Luke 19: 4). 7. Mustard seed (Matthew 13: 31, 32). 8. Apples (Proverbs 25: 11). 9. Mulberry (1 Chronicles 14: 14). 10. Willow (Psalm 137: 1, 2).

WATER

1. Who had trouble over water rights?

2. Who made a tunnel through one of the hills of Jerusalem to bring water into a new pool?

3. What water in Palestine is the saltiest in the world?

4. From what famous well did Jesus drink when on one of His journeys?

5. On what water did Jesus walk one night?

6. Who was it who said that "whosoever shall give you a cup of water . . . shall not lose his reward"?

7. Who was it that had a romance begin by his watering of some sheep?

8. Who stopped up the wells after the death of Abraham, hoping to drive the Hebrews from the country?

9. Which is the longest rain on record?

10. What water is mentioned as being in heaven?

Answers: 1. Abraham had trouble with Abimelech (Genesis 21: 25-30), and Isaac with the herdsmen of Gerar (Genesis 26: 18-25). 2. Hezekiah (2 Kings 20: 20). 3. The Salt Sea, commonly called the Dead Sea. 4. Jacob's well (John 4: 5-29). 5. The Sea of Galilee (Matthew 14: 22-33). 6. Jesus (Mark 9: 41). 7. Moses (Exodus 2: 16-21). 8. The Philistines (Genesis 26: 18). 9. When the flood came (Genesis 7: 12). 10. The "river of water of life" (Revelation 22: 1).

WEATHER

Fill the blanks.

1. A _____ was the occasion for the death of Job's children (Job 1:19).
2. During the days of Ahab, there was a great _____ (1 Kings 17:1-7).
3. When Elijah, on Mt. Carmel, sent his servant to look toward the sea, all that he saw was a _____ (1 Kings 18:44).
4. A great _____ occurred soon after the servant made his report to Elijah (1 Kings 18:45).
5. A great _____ storm contributed to the defeat of the enemies of Israel at Beth-horon (Joshua 10:11).
6. The evil cities of Sodom and Gomorrah were destroyed by _____ (Genesis 19:24).
7. "When it is evening, ye say, It will be _____ weather: for the sky is red" (Matthew 16:2).
8. God knew, long before man did, the value of _____, for He said to Job, "Hast thou entered into the treasures of the _____?" (Job 38:22).
9. "And when ye see the south wind blow, ye say, There will be _____; and it cometh to pass" (Luke 12:55).
10. "As he that taketh away a garment in _____ weather, ... so is he that singeth songs to an heavy heart" (Proverbs 25:20).